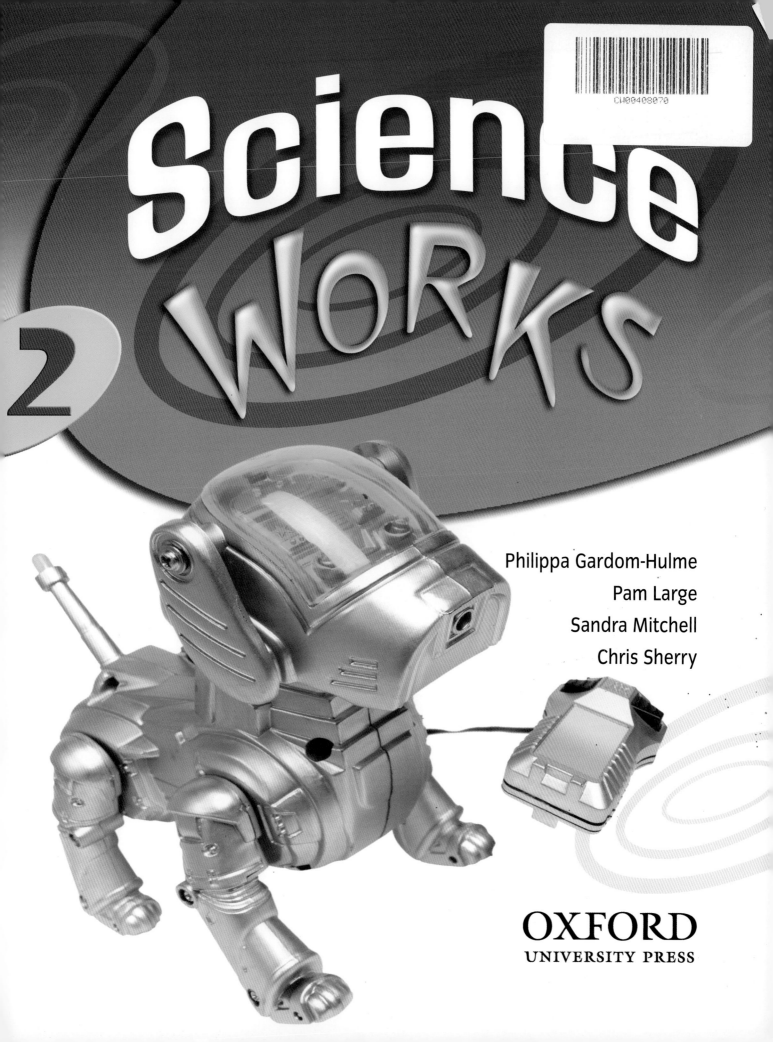

Science works

2

Philippa Gardom-Hulme

Pam Large

Sandra Mitchell

Chris Sherry

OXFORD

UNIVERSITY PRESS

OXFORD
UNIVERSITY PRESS

Great Clarendon Street, Oxford OX2 6DP

Oxford University Press is a department of the University of Oxford.
It furthers the University's objective of excellence in research, scholarship,
and education by publishing worldwide in

Oxford   New York

Auckland   Cape Town   Dar es Salaam   Hong Kong   Karachi
Kuala Lumpur   Madrid   Melbourne   Mexico City   Nairobi
New Delhi   Shanghai   Taipei   Toronto

With offices in

Argentina   Austria   Brazil   Chile   Czech Republic   France   Greece
Guatemala   Hungary   Italy   Japan   Poland   Portugal   Singapore
South Korea   Switzerland   Thailand   Turkey   Ukraine   Vietnam

British Library Cataloguing in Publication Data

Data available

ISBN-13: 9780-19-915250-6

10 9 8 7 6 5 4 3

Printed in China by Printplus

Paper used in the production of this book is a natural, recyclable product made
from wood grown in sustainable forests. The manufacturing process conforms to
the environmental regulations to the country of origin.

Acknowledgments
The Publisher would like to thank the following for permission to reproduce
photographs:

P6t STEVIE GRAND / SCIENCE PHOTO LIBRARY; P6m MEDI-MATION/SCIENCE
PHOTO LIBRARY; P6b Hattie Young / Science Photolibrary; P6l P8t Richard Drew/
Associated press; P8m GUSTOIMAGES / SCIENCE PHOTO LIBRARY; P8b HYBRID
MEDICAL ANIMATION / SCIENCE PHOTO LIBRARY P9 MATT MEADOWS, PETER
ARNOLD INC./SCIENCE PHOTO LIBRARY P10t Augustin Ochsenreiter/ Associated
Press; P10b STEVE GSCHMEISSNER / SCIENCE PHOTO LIBRARY; P12t SAMUEL
ASHFIELD / SCIENCE PHOTO LIBRARY;P13 BSIP VEM / SCIENCE PHOTO LIBRARY;
P14t Robin nelson / Alamy; P15t Steve Gschmeissner / Science Photolibrary;
P15m Cordelia Molloy / Science Photolibrary; P16t GUSTOIMAGES / SCIENCE
PHOTO LIBRARY;P16m Maximilian Stock Ltd / Science Photolibrary;P17 Eddie
Gerald / Alamy; P19m Aj Photo / Hpr Bullion / Science Photolibrary; P20t Andres
Peiro Palmer/iStock; P20m EYE OF SCIENCE / SCIENCE PHOTO LIBRARY; P20b
NIBSC / SCIENCE PHOTO LIBRARY P21t ROGER HARRIS / SCIENCE PHOTO
LIBRARY; P21m KARSTEN SCHNEIDER / SCIENCE PHOTO LIBRARY; P21lWESTERN
OPHTHALMIC HOSPITAL / SCIENCE PHOTO LIBRARY; P22t AJ PHOTO / SCIENCE
PHOTO LIBRARY P22ml DR P. MARAZZI / SCIENCE PHOTO LIBRARY; P22mr DR
TONY BRAIN / SCIENCE PHOTO LIBRARY; P22l JUERGEN BERGER / SCIENCE
PHOTO LIBRARY; P23t SCIENCE PHOTO LIBRARY P23l SAM OGDEN / SCIENCE
PHOTO LIBRARY; P24 LEA PATERSON / SCIENCE PHOTO LIBRARY; P24m VOLKER
STEGER/SCIENCE PHOTO LIBRARY; P24l Lester V Bergman/Corbis UK Ltd; P25t
ALAIN DEX, PUBLIPHOTO DIFFUSION / SCIENCE PHOTO LIBRARY; P25l TH
FOTO-WERBUNG / SCIENCE PHOTO LIBRARY; P26t MARK CLARKE / SCIENCE
PHOTO LIBRARY; Page 26m SATURN STILLS / SCIENCE PHOTO LIBRARY; P26b
DR P. MARAZZI / SCIENCE PHOTO LIBRARY; P27t TIM VERNON, LTH NHS TRUST
/ SCIENCE PHOTO LIBRARY; P27m DR P. MARAZZI / SCIENCE PHOTO LIBRARY;
P27l CC STUDIO / SCIENCE PHOTO LIBRARY; P28t Duncan Walker/iStock;
P28m BSIP, MANCEAU / SCIENCE PHOTO LIBRARY; P28b AJ PHOTO / SCIENCE
PHOTO LIBRARY; P29t AJ PHOTO / SCIENCE PHOTO LIBRARY; P29l Yuri Arcurs/
Dreamstime.com; P30t NASA / SCIENCE PHOTO LIBRARY; P30l TEK IMAGE /
SCIENCE PHOTO LIBRARY; P31t DR YORGOS NIKAS / SCIENCE PHOTO LIBRARY;
P32l PASQUALE SORRENTINO / SCIENCE PHOTO LIBRARY; P32t NASA; P32m
ROY FONTAINE / SCIENCE PHOTO LIBRARY; P32b Naturepl.com/Tim MacMillan/
John Downer; P33t WAYNE LAWLER / SCIENCE PHOTO LIBRARY; P33l BRITISH
ANTARCTIC SURVEY / SCIENCE PHOTO LIBRARY; P34t DR JEREMY BURGESS
/ SCIENCE PHOTO LIBRARY P34m SHEILA TERRY / SCIENCE PHOTO LIBRARY;
P34bl SIMON FRASER / SCIENCE PHOTO LIBRARY; P34br GEORGETTE DOUWMA /

SCIENCE PHOTO LIBRARY; P35t STEVE ALLEN / SCIENCE PHOTO LIBRARY; P35ml
WILLIAM ERVIN / SCIENCE PHOTO LIBRARY; P35mr WILLIAM ERVIN / SCIENCE
PHOTO LIBRARY; P36t South African Tourism / Nigel Dennis; P36l Chris Fourie/
Dreamstime.com; P38 ALAN & SANDY CAREY / SCIENCE PHOTO LIBRARY; P40t
ROBIN TOWNSEND / AGSTOCKUSA / SCIENCE PHOTO LIBRARY; P40l DAVID
CAMPIONE / SCIENCE PHOTO LIBRARY; P42t MAURO FERMARIELLO / SCIENCE
PHOTO LIBRARY; P42l TEK IMAGE / SCIENCE PHOTO LIBRARY; P43t PASCAL
GOETGHELUCK / SCIENCE PHOTO LIBRARY; P44t; Crystal Kirk/Dreamstime; P44m
MITCH REARDON / SCIENCE PHOTO LIBRARY; P44b JEFF LEPORE / SCIENCE
PHOTO LIBRARY; P45t LOUISE MURRAY / SCIENCE PHOTO LIBRARY; P46t LINDA
WRIGHT / SCIENCE PHOTO LIBRARY; P46m MARK NEWMAN / SCIENCE PHOTO
LIBRARY; P46b RITA NANNINI / SCIENCE PHOTO LIBRARY; P48t MARK CLARKE /
SCIENCE PHOTO LIBRARY; P48m TONY CAMACHO / SCIENCE PHOTO LIBRARY;
P48lm Ravi Tahilramani/iStock; P48lm; Ekaterina Cherkashina/Dreamstime; P49
Butinova Elena/iStock; P50t; EYE OF SCIENCE / SCIENCE PHOTO LIBRARY; P50l
STEVE TAYLOR / SCIENCE PHOTO LIBRARY; P51tl MARK GIBSON / AGSTOCKUSA /
SCIENCE PHOTO LIBRARY; P51tr GARRY WATSON / SCIENCE PHOTO LIBRARY; P51l
PHILIPPE PSAILA / SCIENCE PHOTO LIBRARY; P52t SCOTT SINKLIER / AGSTOCKUSA
/ SCIENCE PHOTO LIBRARY; P52l COLIN CUTHBERT / SCIENCE PHOTO LIBRARY;
P53t TON KINSBERGEN / SCIENCE PHOTO LIBRARY; P54tl Alistair Fuller/
Associated Press; P54tr Natasja Weitsz/Contributor/ Getty Images;P54m The Art
Archive; 54b sciencephotos/Alamy; P57 tm Photolibrary; P57tr Triff/Shutterstock;
P57bl Denise Torres/Istockphoto; P57br Stas Perov/ Istockphoto; P58t Alamy;P58b
Kaspars Grinvalds/Shutterstock;P59 Dmitriy Eremenkov/iStockP61tr David H.
Lewis; P61tl ADAM HART-DAVIS / SCIENCE PHOTO LIBRARYP61br Bigstockphoto;
P63t Jgroup/Big Stock Photo; P63t Mark Schneider/Visuals Unlimited/Getty
images; P63m Intelligent Energy; P63b Antonia Reeve; P65m Sean /TheShaman/
Shutterstock; P65lr VAUGHAN FLEMING / SCIENCE PHOTO LIBRARY; P66b Ria
Novosti / Science Photo Library; P71 Oxford University Press; P74tl Les polders/
Alamy; P74tr Nick Hanna/Alamy; P75 MARTYN F. CHILLMAID / SCIENCE PHOTO
LIBRARY; P76 CHARLES D. WINTERS / SCIENCE PHOTO LIBRARY; P77t ANDREW
LAMBERT PHOTOGRAPHY / SCIENCE PHOTO LIBRARY; P77b ASTRID & HANS-
FRIEDER MICHLER / SCIENCE PHOTO LIBRARY; P78t Clynt Garnham/Alamy; P78m
Magus/Alamy; P78l istockphoto; P79t Keith M Law/Alamy; P79t Antonio Oquias
From Philippines/123RF; P80; Ramon Berk/Dreamstime.com; P81t Martyn F.
Chillmaid; P82 ANDREW LAMBERT PHOTOGRAPHY / SCIENCE PHOTO LIBRARY;
P83 Color China Photo/Associated Press; P86t Associated Press; P86l Irochka/
Dreamstime.com;P88 b Dea/A.Rizzi/De Agostini Picture Library/Getty images;
P89t Romanchuck Dimitry/Shutterstock; P89b Zsolt Biczó/Istockphoto; P90
BERNHARD EDMAIER / SCIENCE PHOTO LIBRARY; P91b Ollirg/Shutterstock; P92t
Roman Pavlik /Shutterstock; P92b Jean-Claude Revy, Ism/Science Photo Library;
P93tl Photographers Direct; P93l SIMON FRASER / SCIENCE PHOTO LIBRARY; P94
Zeresenay Alemseged;P96t Tim Graham/Alamy; P97 Dirk Wiersma/Science Photo
Library; P97b Martyn F. Chillmaid / Science Photo Library;P98tr Per Lindgren/Rex
Features; P98tr Vasiliy Ganzha/Shutterstock; P99b Vasiliy Ganzha/Shutterstock;
P100 m Colin Palmer Photography/Alamy; P102t Oleg Kozlov/Dreamstime;
P102b Ivan Hunter Photography/Brand X Pictures/Jupiter images; P103t Tomasz
Trojanowski/Shutterstock; P103l Irena Debevc/iStock; P108t Edward Kinsman /
Science Photolibrary;P108mr Martin Green/Dreamstime.com; P108b Dr Ray Clark
& Mervyn Goff/Science Photolibrary P109tl Cordelia Molloy /Science Photo library;
P112 NASA / SCIENCE PHOTO LIBRARY; P113 Science Photolibrary; P113vt NASA; P113b
NASA; P114tm felix140800/Istockphoto; P114tr Aleksander Bolbot/Dreamstime.
com; P114b Kativ/Istockphoto; P116tr Steven Robertson/Istockphoto; P116 bm
Andrew Lambert Photography/Science Photolibrary; P118t Erich Schrempp/Science
Photolibrary; P118b Tek Image/Science Photolibrary; P120 SCIENCE PHOTO
LIBRARY;P121t Andrew Lambert Photography/Science Photolibrary; P123tm
Ian Boddy/Science Photolibrary; P124t Dainis Derics/Dreamstime.com; P124ml
Strauski/Dreamstime.com; P124mr Stephen Coburn/Dreamstime.com; P124b
Scott Camazine/Science Photo Library; P125tr John Greim/Science Photolibrary;
P125ml Philippe Psaila/Photolibrary;P126t Stephan Zabel/iStock;P126b Steve Allen/
Science Photolibrary; P128t Jack Sullivan/Alamy; P128m Bryce Duffy/Corbis; P129t
Guy Edwardes Photography/Alamy; P129m Christoph Wilhelm/Corbis/Jupiter
Image; P130m Dynamic Graphics/Jupiter images; P130b Compound Security
Systems; P131 Martin Ruegner/Jupiter Images; P132m Brian Bell/Science Photo
Library; P132bl Dr Najeeb Layyous / Science Photo Library; P133b David J.Green/
Alamy; P136t lovleah/Istockphoto; P136m Michael Rolands/Shutterstock; P137bl
Premium Stock/Corbis; P138b The Print Collector/Alamy; P139 Inspirestock/Jupiter
images;P140t Kim Karpeles/Alamy; P141t Alexander Sakhatovsky/Shutterstock;
P145tl www.reddevilsonline.com; P144b Kelly-Mooney Photography/Corbis; P144c
John Martin, The Flambards Experience; P145 www.reddevilsonline.com; P146b
Maksym Gorpenyuk/Dreamstime; P148tl Ffotograff65/Dreamstime; P149m Colin
McWilliam/UK rides; P149bl NASA.

Cover images: Photodisc

In a few cases we have been unable to trace the copyright holder prior
to publication. If notified the publishers will be pleased to amend the
acknowledgements in any future edition.

Figurative illustrations are by Rui Ricardo at Folio Art and technical illustrations
are by Q2A Media and Mark Walker.

How to use Science Works

This book is called *Science Works* because it shows you how scientists work out their ideas about the world, and how science can be put to work in everyday life.

It will help you:
- Develop your understanding of scientific ideas
- Work out scientific ideas for yourself using results from investigations
- See how science is used in everyday life
- Think about how we can use science for the best

The book has two types of pages. Most are like this:

'Learn about' lists your objectives for the topic

'How do we...' boxes tell you something about how scientists work out their ideas

'Brainache' boxes have curious questions on the topic (and their answers!)

'Green' sections revise ideas from Key Stage 2

'Red' headings are to make you think harder!

'Amber' sections move on to new ideas

'Get this' boxes tell what you should know from the topic

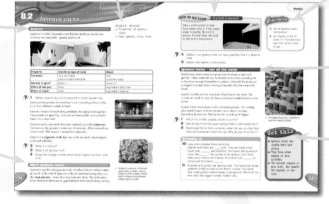

At the end of every unit there is a page called 'How Science Works' which looks at science in action. This might be how science is used in jobs or how science might affect our lives and how we can use it for the best.

All the key words you need to know are in **bold** and they are all defined in a glossary at the end of the book. You'll also find an index right at the back to help you find the information you want.

We hope *Science Works* will help you think about science, understand it and, above all, enjoy it.

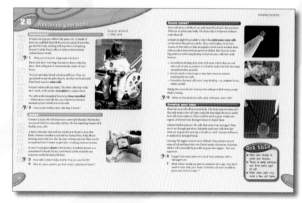

Contents

shows which are the special 'How Science Works' pages (but you'll find out about how science works on other pages too).

Physics

Staying alive

Learn about
- Respiration in cells
- The role of blood

Emergency

Beth isn't breathing and her heart has stopped beating. She's having a **heart attack**. The **paramedics** are trying to save her. One squeezes air into her lungs. Another presses and releases her chest. This pushes blood around her body until they can restart her heart.

Someone has a heart attack every 2 minutes in the UK. Heart attacks cause 1 in 5 deaths.

 1 Beth's heart stopped. Why is that serious?

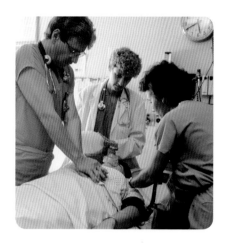

Cut off from supplies

Your heart can beat 100 000 times a day. Each heartbeat pumps blood to every part of your body.

Your cells need energy to stay alive and they get it from glucose and oxygen. Blood collects glucose from digested food and oxygen from your lungs. It delivers the glucose and oxygen to every cell.

Heart muscles work together to pump blood. The muscles are made of cells. Beth's heart attack started when some of these muscle cells ran out of energy and stopped working. The blood vessel that supplied them was blocked by a blood clot. The cells didn't get any oxygen so they died.

Beth was lucky. Her heart restarted. It wasn't too badly damaged. 50% of heart attack victims live for another 10 years.

 2 Why do cells need a good blood supply?

3 What happens during a heart attack?

Struck down

Jo's left arm is paralysed. She had a stroke. A clot blocked a blood vessel in her brain, and the nerve cells there that made her arm move died. The physiotherapist is helping her to get some movement back.

In the UK, somebody has a stroke every 4 minutes.

 4 How is a stroke similar to a heart attack?

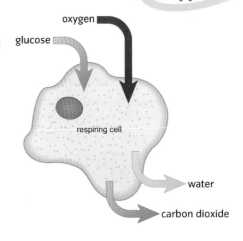

Staying alive

Cells can't store energy. They release it when they need it using a chemical reaction called **respiration**. Glucose from your food reacts with oxygen from your lungs.

Your blood takes the waste products away. You breathe out carbon dioxide through your lungs and any water your body doesn't need goes into your urine.

 5 What gets used up during respiration?

6 Why do you breathe out more carbon dioxide than you breathe in?

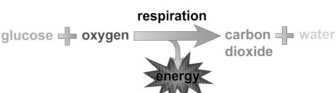

Your cells use the energy from respiration to keep you warm, stay alive, grow and repair themselves. Some cells use energy for movement.

7 List four things muscle cells need energy for.

How do we know... that living things respire?

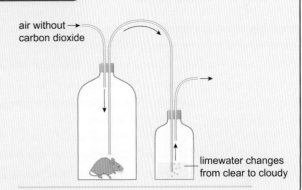

The diagram shows a rat in a jar. No carbon dioxide enters the rat's jar, but air from the jar turns **limewater** cloudy. This shows it has carbon dioxide in it.

The limewater stays clear when a control experiment is done with an empty jar.

8 What evidence is there that the rat is respiring?

9 Why is it important to do a control experiment?

Respiration and burning

The equations for respiration and for burning glucose are the same. Both processes turn a fuel (glucose) and oxygen into carbon dioxide and water, and they both release energy. But cells control the energy release so they don't get hot.

 10 What is the same about burning glucose and respiration?

Summing up

11 Are heart attacks and strokes always fatal?

12 Why does respiration take place in every cell?

13 When you do something very active like running, more blood flows to your leg muscles. Explain why.

14 How can you prove that a living thing is respiring?

Get this

- Blood brings glucose and oxygen to every cell.
- During respiration they react to release energy.
- The reaction produces carbon dioxide and water.

Breathing

Champion lungs

In 2007 Tom Sietas broke the Guinness World Record for holding his breath under water. He lasted 15 minutes. Don't try this at home!

Tom filled his lungs with pure oxygen. He kept very still. The cold water made his heart beat more slowly and cut the blood supply to his arms and legs. That saved oxygen for his heart and brain.

 1 Why do all your tissues need oxygen?

Swapping gases

Are you sitting still? If so, you're probably taking about 15 breaths per minute. Each breath draws fresh air into your lungs. As your blood passes through them its **red blood cells** fill up with oxygen.

At the same time, carbon dioxide from respiring cells moves from your blood to the air. The blood swaps, or **exchanges**, its waste carbon dioxide gas for oxygen gas – so the process is called **gas exchange**.

When your cells need more oxygen you breathe faster to take in more air, and your heart rate increases to push blood through your lungs more quickly.

 2 What happens to the blood in your lungs?

Sponges full of blood

Your lungs are soft and spongy. The ribs surround them and protect them from damage.

When you breathe in, muscles make your chest bigger to draw air in through your mouth and nose. When the muscles relax your chest springs back to its normal size, and air is pushed out.

 3 Where in your body are your lungs?
     4 How do muscles make you breathe in?

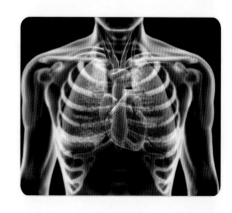

Millions of branches

Your windpipe comes down from your nose and mouth, divides into two and keeps dividing to form millions of tiny branches.

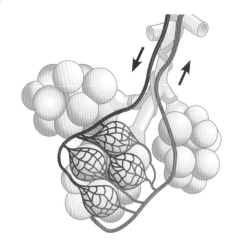

At the end of each branch is a cluster of air pockets, called **alveoli**, surrounded by a fine network of blood vessels. The walls of the blood vessels and alveoli are so thin that gas molecules can move from one to the other easily by **diffusion**.

Blood pumped to the lungs from the heart is short of oxygen. It goes back to the heart full of oxygen to be pumped round the body. Blood that lacks oxygen is shown as blue in this diagram but it is really just a slightly darker red.

 5 What happens to carbon dioxide as blood flows around the alveoli?

Smoke damage

Normal lungs are soft and pink, but these are a smoker's lungs. They are thick with tar and can't take in much oxygen.

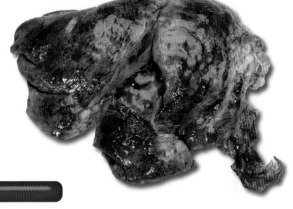

Smoke contains hundreds of different chemicals. Some damage your lungs. Others increase your risk of having cancer, heart disease or a stroke. On average smokers live 13 years less than non-smokers.

 6 List three ways cigarettes can harm you.

It's all in the area!

You have about 300 million alveoli. If you spread out their walls they could cover a tennis court. At any moment, a quarter of a mug of blood flows over this large surface area. It is spread very thinly, so oxygen diffuses quickly to every red cell.

 7 Why do lungs need a large surface area?

Summing up

8 What is the difference between breathing and respiration?

9 Why do your heart rate and breathing get faster when you run?

10 Most organs sink in water, but lungs float. Suggest why.

11 Imagine you are an oxygen molecule that has just been breathed in. Describe the route you take to get to the blood.

12 Many people think, wrongly, that blood is blue when it is short of oxygen. Why?

Get this

- Lungs pump air in and out of our bodies.
- In gas exchange oxygen and carbon dioxide pass between the blood and air through the alveoli.

Delivering supplies

Sudden death

Oetzi died 5300 years ago but his body was preserved by ice. Now hospital scanners have revealed how he died. An arrow pierced an **artery** in his shoulder. Blood spurted out and he died within minutes.

Arteries are strong blood vessels. They carry blood away from your heart. Each heartbeat gives blood a hard push, so the blood in arteries is under pressure and moving fast. That's why it spurts out so quickly if you damage one.

1 What are arteries?

2 Why does blood spurt out of a damaged artery?

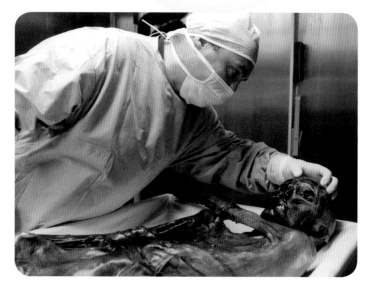

A round trip

Two big arteries leave your heart. One takes blood to your lungs to collect oxygen, and the other carries blood to the rest of the body.

Blood carrying oxygen comes back from the lungs and the heart pushes it round the rest of the body. At the same time it pushes blood from the body towards the lungs.

On each trip round the body a single blood cell goes through the heart twice.

3 Why is your heart called a double pump?

4 You lift a heavy bag. Respiration in the muscle cells in your arms makes carbon dioxide. How does it get to your lungs?

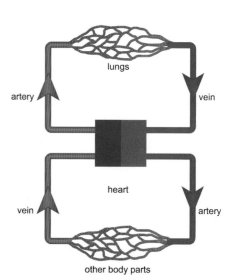

lungs

artery

vein

heart

vein

artery

other body parts

key
- blood carrying more oxygen
- blood carrying less oxygen

Supplying the cells

The arteries divide again and again into smaller and smaller blood vessels. The smallest are **capillaries** like this one.

Every cell in the body is close to a capillary. Red blood cells go through them in single file. Capillaries are so thin that small molecules like glucose and oxygen can diffuse out to the body cells around them.

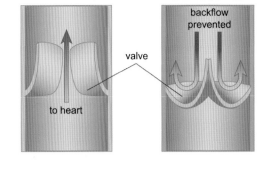

backflow prevented

valve

to heart

Capillaries join up to form wide blood vessels called **veins**, which return blood to your heart. Blood travels slowly in veins. Flaps called **valves** act like one-way doors to stop blood flowing backwards.

Two veins enter your heart. One brings blood back from the lungs; the other brings it from the rest of the body.

When you cut yourself you have usually damaged capillaries. The bleeding soon stops. If blood flows out in a smooth stream, without a pulse, you have cut a vein.

5 What are the main differences between veins and arteries?

6 Why do the veins in your legs need valves?

7 Why is it much easier to stop blood flowing from a vein than an artery?

How do we know... the route blood takes?

Around 2000 years ago, a Greek philosopher called Galen said that the heart made blood and pumped it to the tissues, where it was used up.

The idea was accepted in Europe until the 1600s when a doctor called William Harvey did experiments on living animals. He watched animals' hearts beating. They pumped out massive amounts of blood. It could never be made that fast. He realised the same blood must keep going round and round.

Years later Syrian manuscripts were translated and Europeans realised that an Islamic doctor, Ibn al-Nafis, had written more or less the same thing 350 years before Harvey's discoveries.

8 What made Harvey doubt Galen's ideas?

9 Why were Ibn al-Nafis' discoveries not known in Europe when he made them?

Get this

- The heart pumps blood out to the lungs and the rest of the body.
- Blood leaves the heart in arteries and returns in veins.
- Capillaries deliver blood to every cell.

Summing up

10 Some blood has just left your lungs. Describe the route it takes to get back to the lungs.

11 Many people think the same blood visits every part of the body before it returns to the heart. What really happens?

Keeping fit

Fitness testing

Nathalie is doing a fitness test. The pads on her chest monitor her heart and the tube in her mouth senses how much oxygen she is using.

Your **fitness** depends on your heart, lungs and blood vessels. The fitter you are, the more they can increase the oxygen and glucose supply to your cells and let your muscles work harder.

 1 Why is blood sent to your muscles faster when you are doing more exercise?

2 Which two organs determine your fitness?

Working harder

Nathalie is running on a treadmill. As she works harder she breathes faster and deeper. Her heart beats so hard she can hear it thumping.

Eventually Nathalie's heart and lungs can't work any harder and the test ends. The table shows how her heart and lungs responded.

 3 What happened to Nathalie's heart rate during the test?

4 How was Nathalie's oxygen intake increased during the test?

Nathalie is pleased with her results. She has only been training for a few months, but her heart is already stronger. Her resting heart rate used to be 80 beats per minute and 190 beats per minute when she started to run.

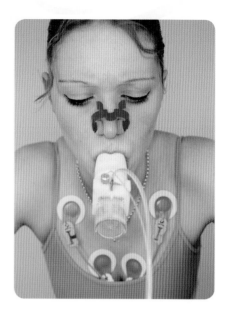

	Start	End
Heart rate in beats per minute	50	150
Breathing rate in breaths per minute	13	39

Her lower heart rate shows that she is fitter. Like any muscle your heart gets stronger when you exercise. This means it can pump more strongly and so doesn't need to pump so often.

To keep fit you should do something energetic for 30 minutes, 5 times a week.

 5 How much exercise do you need to stay healthy?

6 How has training affected Nathalie's heart?

7 Look at the graph. How much did Nathalie's oxygen uptake change during the test?

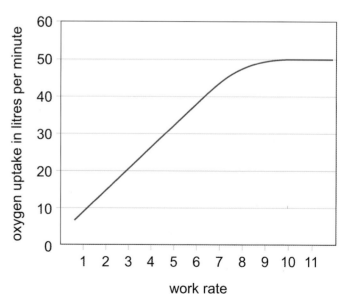

Up against resistance

Nathalie's dad isn't so fit. He has **plaque** in his arteries which makes them narrower. His heart has to work harder to push blood through them.

The yellow plaque in this artery is a mixture of fat, cholesterol and blood cells. Plaque starts forming when you are in your teens.

Sometimes plaque breaks away from an artery wall, a clot forms and the artery is blocked. If it leads to your heart or brain, you have a heart attack or stroke.

Fortunately, a healthy lifestyle lowers the chance of this happening.

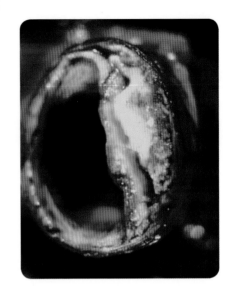

8   What is the plaque in your arteries made from?

9   How can plaque harm your health?

How do we know... that your lifestyle affects your health?

The British Regional Heart Study compared 7000 people for 25 years to look for clues. Those who had heart attacks or strokes had more of these risk factors.

Risk factors

- smoking
- being overweight
- no exercise, unhealthy food
- high salt intake, excess alcohol
- inherited genes

Other studies show that inhaling smoke from other people's cigarettes is also a risk factor.

More young people are having heart attacks than ever before.

10   Are there any risk factors that people can't control?

11   Suggest why more young people have heart attacks now.

12   How might a smoking ban affect the number of heart attacks?

13   Do you think that the evidence from this survey is reliable? Why?

Get this

- Exercise makes your heart and lungs work harder to deliver oxygen.
- Exercise strengthens your heart muscles.
- Plaque in arteries puts a strain on your heart and can cause a blockage.

Summing up

14   Why does exercise make your heart stronger?

15   How can waste carbon dioxide be taken from your muscles more quickly when you exercise?

16   Why is plaque in arteries dangerous?

17   How can you reduce your risk of having a heart attack?

Break down

Lucy isn't well. There's something wrong with her **digestive system**. She isn't getting enough **nutrients** and her doctor wants to find out why.

The pill she's taking has a camera in it. It will take 500 000 pictures as it travels through her system.

The job of the digestive system is to turn the food you eat into forms which your body can use.

Most of the food you eat, like **starch, fats** and **proteins**, is made of big complex molecules (see page 75). Digestion breaks them down into simple nutrients like **glucose** which your body cells can use. These pass into your blood and are carried to every cell.

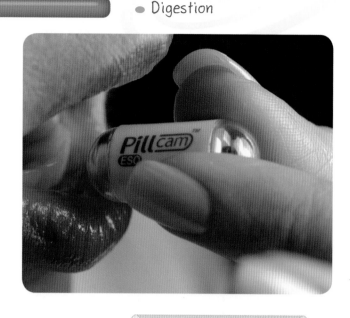

1   What happens to food in your gut?
2   How do nutrients like glucose get to your cells?

Beginning the journey

Lucy's **saliva** makes the camera slippery, so it slides down her **gullet** easily. Saliva also contains an **enzyme**. Enzymes break down large molecules into small ones. The enzyme in saliva starts to break down starch as you chew.

3   Give two reasons why you need saliva.
4   Why should you chew your food?

When it reaches Lucy's **stomach** the camera gets thrown around.

The stomach acts like a mixer. It blends the food with another enzyme to make a smooth paste. Then it squirts it into the **small intestine**.

5   What happens to food in your stomach?

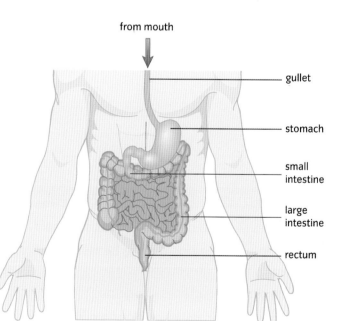

from mouth

gullet

stomach

small intestine

large intestine

rectum

Getting into the blood

If you unravelled your small intestine it would be four times longer than your body, so it is really not small but very big! Most large molecules get broken down in your small intestine.

Muscles around the intestine squeeze food along and mix it with more enzymes.

These finger-like **villi** line the inside walls. They are 1 mm tall. Like the alveoli on page 9 they have a good blood supply. If you flattened them all out you'd also see that they have a huge surface area. This is where nutrients are absorbed into the blood.

Lucy's camera showed that her villi were very short. That's why she couldn't absorb all her nutrients. The problem is caused by an allergy to wheat. She will get better when she stops eating wheat.

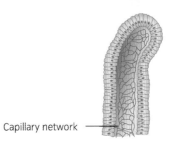

Capillary network

6 How is food moved through the small intestine?

7 How do villi help nutrients get into your blood?

Getting extra nutrients

When a meal gets to the **large intestine** there is nothing left of the food but **fibre**. You can't break fibre down, but you still need to eat it. It makes food easier to push along, so it stops you getting **constipated**.

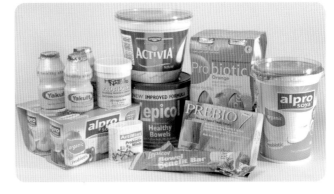

This part of the gut is full of friendly bacteria. They live off the fibre and make important vitamins that we can absorb. **Probiotic** foods, like live yoghurt, give you extra bacteria.

The walls of the large intestine absorb water to turn the mixture of fibre and bacteria into solid waste called **faeces**. It is stored in the **rectum** until you are ready to go to the toilet.

8 Why do you need fibre?

9 Live yoghurt contains bacteria. How could it be good for you?

10 What do faeces contain?

Summing up

11 Describe the route fibre takes through your body.

12 Why do most foods need to be digested?

13 What do the enzymes in your gut do?

14 Where do nutrients get absorbed into the blood?

15 What two jobs does the large intestine do?

Get this

- Digestion breaks down complex food molecules to small nutrient molecules we can use.
- Villi in the small intestine absorb these molecules.

Fuel and building blocks

Terry wants to be good at his sport. He's training hard and building muscles, so he needs to feed himself well.

Terry eats plenty of carbohydrates for energy. He also makes sure he gets enough proteins for growth and repair, but not too much fat. He knows some types of fat have been linked to heart disease.

 1 What sorts of food give you energy?

2 Which nutrients do you need for growth and repair?

Healthy choices

Terry uses this food wheel to balance his diet. It shows him how much to eat from each food group.

Most people get protein and fat from meat, fish and dairy products, but Terry is a vegetarian. He gets proteins from beans, nuts and cereals, and he gets fats from vegetable oils.

Terry eats bread and pasta but most of his carbohydrates come from fresh fruit and vegetables. That way he knows he will get the vitamins, minerals and fibre he needs.

 3 Name four different sources of protein.

4 What sorts of food give you carbohydrates?

5 Why is it important to eat a variety of different foods?

Vitamins and minerals

You only need small amounts of **vitamins** and **minerals**. But if you don't get enough it can affect your health. These are some of the most important ones, and the symptoms you can get if they are missing.

Too much can also be a bad thing. Most people get too much of one mineral – salt. It can increase their risk of having high blood pressure, a heart attack or a stroke.

Vitamin or mineral	Possible symptoms if missing
A	blindness
B group	exhaustion, depression
C	bleeding gums
D	weak bones
calcium	weak bones
iron	exhaustion
potassium	heart failure

 6 Ben slipped over and broke his leg. What could have made his bones so brittle?

Topping up your blood sugar

The carbohydrates you eat come in two different forms. There are *starches* with big molecules and *sugars*, like glucose, with small ones (see page 14). Digestion breaks down starch to glucose.

Glucose doesn't need digesting, so it passes straight into your blood. Cells can use it for respiration straight away. But a quick burst of energy leaves you feeling tired later. Starch digests slowly so it releases less glucose at a time over a longer period.

Spare glucose molecules are stored in your muscles and liver until you need them. When these stores are full the rest is converted to fat.

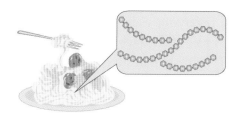

7 How is glucose different from starch?

8 What happens if you eat more carbohydrates than you need?

Building with proteins

Your whole body is made of proteins. Proteins are long molecules made of chains of **amino acids**. When they break down in your gut, the amino acids separate. There are 20 different ones. Cells join them in different combinations to make every protein they need. It's a bit like building thousands of different models with just 20 different types of Lego brick.

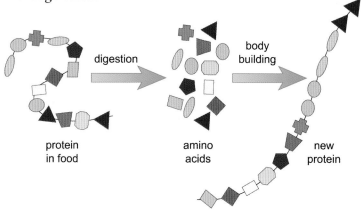

protein in food → digestion → amino acids → body building → new protein

9 How does your body build the proteins it needs for growth and repair?

Summing up

10 List the nutrients a healthy diet must contain. Say what each is used for and name one type of food it is found in.

11 Plant proteins are very different from human proteins. Explain why that does not matter.

12 Why is it good to eat starchy foods for breakfast?

13 You can manage for weeks without food if you need to. Explain how.

Get this

- A balanced diet contains carbohydrates, protein, fats, minerals, vitamins and fibre.
- Cells use nutrients for respiration and to build proteins.

HOW SCIENCE WORKS

Favourite foods

Think of your favourite food. Is it chips, pizza, chocolate or ice cream? If it is you are in good company. We inherit a taste for sweet, fatty foods. They make us relax.

Everyone except babies also likes the taste of salt. Sugar and salt are plentiful now but were hard for our ancestors to find. These cravings helped them survive by making them search for salt deposits and foods packed with energy.

Bitter foods have the opposite effect. They make you want to spit them out. Most poisonous plants taste bitter, so that's useful.

You learn what not to eat quickly. If you are sick soon after you've eaten something, it puts you off that food for life.

1 What tastes do newborns prefer?

2 Why is it useful if harmful foods make you feel bad?

Learning from others

Juan loves red hot chilli peppers. He couldn't stand them when he was young but his parents kept giving him a taste and he soon learned to like them.

Most people won't eat eyeballs, testicles (testes) or caterpillars – even though they are packed with nutrients. But people from some cultures learn to find these tasty.

You often grow to like things you see other people eating. Advertisers know this so they show foods being eaten by people you admire.

3 Most people hate the taste of coffee when they first taste it. Why do they end up liking it?

4 Why are famous footballers used in adverts for snacks that students might buy?

Convenience

Carl feels hungry. His parents are out and there's nothing in the house to eat – only stuff that needs cooking. He can't face walking to the supermarket, so he gets a takeaway, or some chocolate. The sugar and fat in them makes him feel good, and it's the easiest option.

5 Describe one thing that might stop you eating healthily.

Shopping

Psychologists study how and why we do what we do.
They find that shoppers **subconsciously** balance the nutrient
content of food against:

- what their families like
- taste
- convenience
- value for money.

Families are buying more ready meals and less fresh foods
– especially for teenagers. These can contain large amounts
of sugar, salt or saturated fats. The Food Standards Agency
recommends that traffic light labelling is used on all processed
foods so we can see what's in them at a glance.

 6 How do people decide which foods to buy?

7 Why are some convenience foods bad for you?

8 Why was the traffic light labelling system introduced?

Making good health easier

In 2006, one-quarter of UK adults were **obese**.

Psychologists say the only way to prevent obesity is
to make fatty and sugary foods harder to buy, and get
people to take more exercise.

Schools make everyone do at least two hours of
physical activity per week and many new offices make
adults use the stairs instead of the lift.

 9 On average people eat less now than they used
to. Suggest why more people have become
obese.

10 Why is exercise one of
the best ways of keeping
weight under control?

Health authorities want you to
choose a healthy balanced diet
and keep fit. Then you will avoid
the risk factors that make heart
disease, strokes and cancer more
common.

Get this

- We are born with a taste for sweet, fatty foods.
- We learn to prefer what those around us eat.
- Convenience plays a big part in deciding what we eat.

Microbes

Yuck

Ben bit into his apple and found it was rotten inside. That's disgusting. He threw the rest away.

Disgust keeps us away from things that could make us ill. Rotten things are decaying. They contain **microbes** and many of these cause diseases. They kill millions of people, and make billions of others sick.

 1   Why should you avoid touching microbes?

Alien cells

You have about 10 trillion cells of your own. Your body carries ten times as many **microbial** cells. They cover your skin and line openings like your mouth and gut.

These are cells from Ben's mouth. Most are microscopic **bacteria**. The large ones are as big as red blood cells. They are a type of **fungus**. Too many of these fungi can cause thrush which covers your mouth with painful white spots.

Huge numbers of bacteria live in your large intestine. Most are good for you. They help you digest your food. 60% of your faeces are made of microbes. They only harm you if they get into your blood.

 2   Which parts of your body carry most microbes?

3   Young children are often curious about their faeces. Why should you teach them not to touch their faeces?

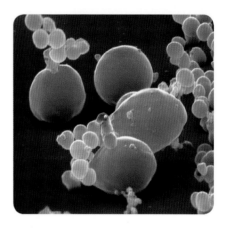

Viruses

Viruses don't have cells. They can't carry out most life processes – like getting nutrition. But they do have genes and they reproduce inside living things, including you.

Most viruses are destructive like the **HIV** viruses on this white blood cell. Viruses cause 60% of human infections.

 4   List two things that make viruses different from plants, animals and other microbes.

Dividing and multiplying

Bacteria make toxins and destroy tissues. One microbe can't do much harm. It's too small. But bacteria keep dividing into two. They can rapidly increase their numbers.

These bacteria are **MRSA**. A third of your class could be carrying them. They are harmless on your skin or in your nose. But they can kill hospital patients if they get into their wounds.

 5   How do bacteria reproduce?

6   Why is it so hard to keep MRSA out of hospitals?

Viruses can multiply even faster than bacteria. They get inside your cells and control them. Each infected cell builds thousands of new virus particles and then dies. These **flu** viruses are bursting out through a dead cell's membrane.

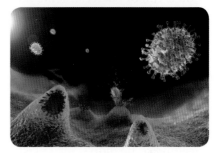

 7   Viruses do not feed, respire or excrete but they can reproduce. Explain how.

Infected

The most common viruses cause colds. Others, like chickenpox, give you a temporary rash and a high temperature. Some viruses, like HIV, can kill.

Many bacteria cause **vomiting** or **diarrhoea**. Others make your tissues red and swollen. Tuberculosis (**TB**) bacteria damage lungs, and bacterial **meningitis** can cause fatal brain damage.

This baby's mum had no symptoms. She didn't know she had **chlamydia** and **gonorrhoea**. These bacteria infect the cells in a woman's **cervix** at the base of her womb. They are passed on during sex. The bacteria got into her baby's eyes and lungs as she was giving birth.

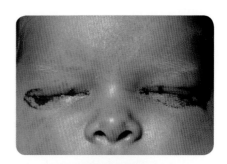

 8   List some common symptoms caused by viruses.

9   Why is it a problem when an infected person has no symptoms?

Summing up

10   List three types of microbes.

11   How can common skin bacteria make people ill?

12   Explain why infections don't make you ill straight away.

13   List four diseases caused by viruses.

14   List two common symptoms caused by bacterial infections.

Get this

- Many bacteria are useful in the right place, or harmless.
- Some bacteria and most viruses are harmful.
- Bacteria reproduce rapidly by dividing. Viruses force cells to make them.

Learn about
- Dealing with microbes

Feeling sick

Jenni went to a barbecue yesterday. Now she feels sick and keeps rushing to the toilet. She has food poisoning.

You can't help eating microbes. They're everywhere. Most are destroyed by the strong hydrochloric **acid** in your stomach. But if food is full of bacteria, some may survive. They get carried through your gut and give you diarrhoea.

 1 What causes food poisoning?

In pain

Sam can't write properly. His finger is swollen and painful. He cut it last week. It stopped bleeding so he didn't put a plaster on it.

When you cut a blood vessel, fibres form in the gap. They trap red blood cells and make a **clot**. This keeps blood in and microbes out until the gap can be repaired. For most cuts this works very well. But some bacteria can dissolve the fibres and slip into your blood. This is what happened to Sam.

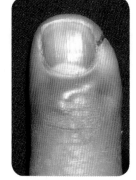

 2 What happened to Sam's cut?
3 Why should cuts be kept clean?

Coughing and sneezing

You suck in microbes every time you breathe, but your lungs are protected. They make a sticky **mucus** that traps microbes, and they have hair-like **cilia** that brush the microbes to your throat to be swallowed.

These yellow bacteria cause pneumonia if they manage to infect lung cells.

Some viruses get past your defences too. They attack cells in your nose or lungs and give you a cold or flu.

 4 How are most microbes kept out of your lungs?
5 Name two sorts of virus that can infect your airways.

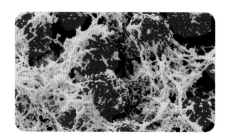

Destroying invaders

White blood cells can combat most infections. They are part of your **immune system**.

White cells destroy microbes in your blood and squeeze through capillary walls to clear bacteria from your tissues.

Some types of white cell just swallow invaders. This one is surrounding the bacteria (pink) with its cytoplasm. Then it will pull them in, digest them and die. The pus from a spot is full of dead white cells.

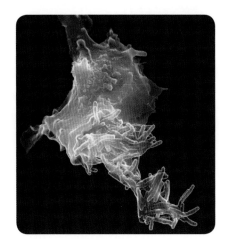

 6 How can white cells destroy bacteria?

7 Why don't white blood cells stay in your blood?

A memory for microbes

Other white cells make chemicals called **antibodies** which help to kill microbes.

You need a different antibody for each type of microbe. The first time a microbe infects you, white cells take a week to make the right antibody. The microbes have time to multiply and make you feel ill, but you destroy them in the end.

If the same type of microbe infects you again, your immune system remembers them. It makes antibodies quickly before their numbers increase. So you don't get ill. You are **immune** to the disease they cause.

 8 What are antibodies?

9 How do you become immune to a disease?

Lost immunity

The HIV virus infects white blood cells and destroys them. It doesn't kill you, but it takes away your defences. Then other microbes like pneumonia and TB can destroy your tissues. HIV infection usually turns into **AIDS (acquired immune deficiency syndrome)**.

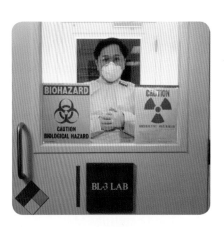

HIV is passed on during sex or when blood, semen or vaginal fluids get into cuts.

 10 What is the connection between HIV and AIDS?

11 Why do people with HIV die from other infections?

Summing up

12 List three ways microbes can enter your body.

13 How are bacteria kept out of your gut, blood and lungs?

14 White cells destroy bacteria in two ways. What are they?

15 Why do you only get diseases like chickenpox once?

Get this

- Body defences keep most microbes out.
- White blood cells usually destroy those that get in.
- Antibodies give you immunity but it takes time to produce them for new microbes.

Keeping clean

Alex has microbes from her **faeces** all over her hands. They will rub off on anything she touches. But a good wash with soap would remove them.

Telephones, remote controls and keyboards are usually covered in microbes – and anything else that gets handled a lot.

Disinfectants and **bleach** destroy bacteria on surfaces, but they damage our body tissues. **Antiseptics** are safe to use on skin.

 1 Why is it important to teach youngsters to wash their hands after going to the toilet?

2 How can you destroy microbes in kitchens and bathrooms?

Dealing with faeces

This robot is checking a pipe for cracks. The pipe takes **sewage** to a **water treatment works**. Sewage is waste water from toilets, sinks and gutters. Microbes are removed before it flows into rivers.

Most UK tap water comes from reservoirs, lakes and rivers. The rest is from wells. It is **sterilised** before it reaches us to destroy any microbes.

 3 Floods make sewers overflow. Why should you avoid touching flood water?

Safe food

How often does your family shop? Unless you shop daily, you need to store food carefully. Most food contamination happens in our homes.

Packaged food comes with a 'use by' date, but microbes grow more quickly when food is warm and damp. These **salmonella** microbes are growing on raw chicken. If they get into your gut they will give you food poisoning.

 4 Why is it important to take fresh meat and chilled ready meals straight home when you buy them?

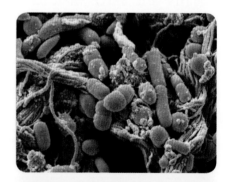

Preventing infection

Sandy has a cold. A virus is reproducing inside her. Her sneeze carries the virus into the air. Anyone near her could breathe it in. But colds can also spread by touch.

Viruses survive for hours on surfaces. Your fingers pick them up when you touch things. They can get into your body if you rub your nose or eyes.

 5   Why should you cover your face when you sneeze?

6   Why is it best to wash your hands more often if someone in your family has a cold?

How do we know... that hands can spread colds?

Scientists took snot from cold sufferers and dripped it into volunteers' eyes and nose. Both methods made volunteers develop colds.

When medical students were watched during a 1 hour lecture, 1 in 3 picked their nose and 1 in 3 rubbed their eyes.

When cold sufferers sneezed, people on the opposite side of the room were rarely infected. If they sneezed and then shook hands with lots of people, colds were spread more widely.

7   Which evidence shows viruses can get in via your eyes?

8   How could colds be passed by hand shaking?

Staying safe

The microbes that cause **sexually transmitted infections (STIs)** are only passed on during sex. They can only survive for a few seconds outside the body. Condoms protect you from most STIs if you use them properly.

The most common STIs are caused by **HPV** viruses. There's no cure.

Chlamydia bacteria cause the most common curable STI. But people often don't notice they've got it. If girls don't get treated in time, it can stop them having a baby later.

 9   Why should you get regular check-ups if you are sexually active?

Summing up

10 List four sources of microbes.

11 Why is it important to keep sewers in good repair?

12 Cholera bacteria cause severe diarrhoea. Where there is no sewage treatment they spread rapidly. Suggest why.

13 'Use by' dates are only a rough guide. Explain why.

14 List four ways of cutting the number of infections you get.

Get this

- We pick up microbes from faeces, contaminated water, food and infected people.
- Good hygiene cuts infection – especially hand washing.

Learn about
- Vaccination and boosting immunity

Feeling bad

Paul's father died last week. He's very depressed and has lost his appetite. He also has a cold and a throat infection.

Unhappiness, stress or a shortage of vitamins and minerals can all weaken your immune system. It is strengthened by regular exercise and 15 minutes in the sun each day – sunshine gives you vitamin D.

In some countries many children don't get enough zinc, iron or vitamin A in their diets. This weakens their immune systems so diseases are more likely to kill them.

 1 List three things that weaken your immune system.

Strengthening your immunity

This baby is 8 weeks old. She's being **immunised**. The jab contains **vaccines**.

Before she goes to school she will have jabs to make her **immune** to some serious diseases: measles, diphtheria, tetanus, whooping cough, polio, pneumonia, blood poisoning and meningitis.

Vaccines contain tiny parts of the microbes. They won't make her ill. But her body will make antibodies against them. If the real microbes infect her in future, her immune system will produce antibodies very quickly and destroy them before they can harm her.

 2 What do vaccines contain?

3 How does immunisation work?

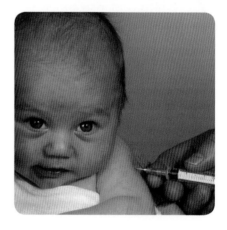

Temporary immunity

Many people get a flu jab every autumn. But there are hundreds of flu viruses and they keep changing, so you need a different jab every year.

Scientists have to predict which viruses will be most common each year. They are trying to make new vaccines that will work for every type of flu.

 4 Why doesn't a flu jab protect you for life?

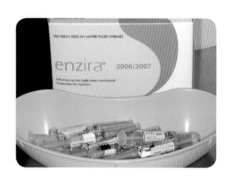

How do we decide which vaccines to give?

The **National Health Service (NHS)** provides vaccines for serious diseases that could affect a lot of people. These vaccines change as scientists develop new ones and old ones are no longer needed.

This woman has smallpox. This disease used to kill more people than any other disease. It was wiped out in the 1970s by immunising millions of people. Now the vaccine is no longer needed.

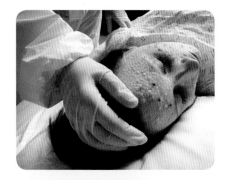

The number of young people with sexually transmitted HPV infections is rising. Some types make warts grow around your penis or vagina – like the one on this finger. Others make women more likely to get cervical cancer when they're older.

Since 2008, 12-year-old girls have been given a new vaccine to protect them from these infections. The jabs cost the NHS about £100 million per year.

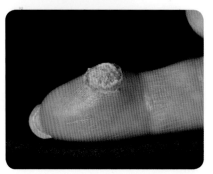

There are no effective vaccines for most STIs.

5 How was the smallpox virus wiped out?

6 Why are girls vaccinated against HPV now?

Dealing with emergencies

Sometimes white blood cells can't cope with an infection and bacteria multiply rapidly. If they make you very ill your doctor can give you an **antibiotic**.

Antibiotics destroy bacteria and make you feel better. But they have no effect on viruses.

The bacteria on this plate are common in hospitals. The tablets are antibiotics. Clear circles show where they have killed the bacteria.

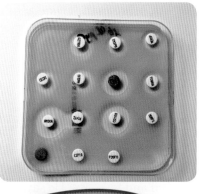

7 How many antibiotics had no effect on the bacteria?

If you have an antibiotic you must finish the tablets, even when you feel better. The toughest bacteria are the last to be killed. If these survive and multiply they will be harder to destroy and will be more **resistant** to the antibiotic. Most antibiotics are useless against MRSA.

Get this

- Low stress, regular exercise and a good diet strengthen your immune system.
- Vaccinations make you immune to particular microbes.
- Antibiotics destroy bacteria but not viruses.

Summing up

8 Why are children immunised before they go to school?

9 Why might the NHS supply different vaccines in future?

10 Why can't antibiotics cure a bad case of flu?

11 How do bacteria become resistant to antibiotics?

Learn about
- Cigarettes, cannabis and alcohol

On top of the world

Josh couldn't feel better. He scored the winning goal. But any sort of exercise makes you feel good – especially when you're part of a team.

Josh never misses a training session, even when the weather's freezing. His **peers** in the team are just as keen. They want to be winners, so **peer pressure** makes them all train hard.

Running round the pitch caused changes in Josh's brain. He will feel good all day. Since he started getting regular exercise he is a lot more confident and gets better grades in school.

1 What makes Josh train hard at football?

2 How does the training affect his mood?

Drugged

Natalie gets up late at the weekend. She smokes a cigarette to wake herself up. Her parents think it's a disgusting habit but all her friends smoke.

The **nicotine** in the cigarette affects Natalie's brain. It makes her feel alert, so it's a **stimulant**. Cigarettes are hard to give up once you've tried them. They are **addictive**. She will need another one very soon. Meanwhile, other chemicals in the smoke are harming her body (see page 9).

3 How does Natalie's cigarette affect her mood?

4 Why are cigarettes hard to give up?

Natalie's brother smokes **cannabis**, an illegal drug. It makes him relaxed and talkative. He says it makes music and colours more intense.

Cannabis changes the way he sees and hear things, so it's an **hallucinogen**. It can also cause panic attacks. Some users become addicted and some develop mental health problems.

Cannabis smoke contains more toxins than tobacco smoke and regular users have more lung damage.

5 How does cannabis affect people's brains?

6 What damage does cannabis do?

Feeling down

Beth has a hangover. Her parents are away so she had friends round last night. They brought drinks with them.

Beth hadn't drunk alcohol before, but she didn't want her friends to know that. They might think she was odd. She drank a lot. At first it made her relax. Then she was sick.

7 How could peer pressure make you start drinking?

Alcohol is a **depressant**, which means it slows your reactions. Drinkers take longer to spot hazards so they shouldn't drive. They would have too many accidents.

Alcohol can also make you aggressive and more likely to take risks. Drinkers often get into fights and have accidents.

8 How does alcohol affect your mood?

Women can drink 3 units of alcohol per day, and men can drink 4, without damaging their health. Drinking more in one day is binge drinking. The extra makes you more likely to get liver damage or heart disease.

9 Why is it dangerous to drink and drive?

10 How many alcopops could an adult safely drink in a day?

11 What health problems does excess alcohol cause?

pint of lager	alcopop	glass of wine	shot of vodka
3	1.5	2	1

▲ Units of alcohol.

How do we know... that peer pressure affects alcohol consumption?

Psychologists found out that students binge drink because they think everyone else drinks a lot. They told students how much their peers really drank. Those who drank less than average didn't change, but those who drank more cut back.

12 How did students respond when they realised they drank more than the average student?

Summing up

13 How does exercise affect your brain?

14 Stimulants, depressants and hallucinogens all affect your brain. Explain what each sort of drug does to your brain.

15 What is peer pressure?

16 Is peer pressure always a bad thing?

17 Drinkers take risks. Why is that a problem?

Get this

- Peer pressure can affect your behaviour.
- Smoking damages your lungs and alcohol damages your liver.
- Both affect your brain.

How Science Works

Unprotected

Connor can't go out without his space suit. A breath of fresh air could kill him. He lives in a hospital. If microbes get into his body, nothing will stop them multiplying. Connor's white blood cells are faulty so his immune system doesn't work.

1 Why can't Connor's body resist infection?

Blood cells don't last long. You have to keep replacing them. New cells grow in marrow in the centre of your bones.

The red and white blood cells look different. They are specialised to suit the jobs they do. But they are both made from bone marrow **stem cells**.

Connor's stem cells are faulty. The white cells they make don't work, so he needs a **transplant** to replace them.

The cells in the transplant have to be **tissue matched** – which means very like his own. Otherwise the new immune system would attack his cells.

2 How could healthy stem cells help Connor?

Saved

Connor is lucky. He will soon have a new baby brother. His brother was tested when he was a tiny embryo. He has matching tissues with healthy stem cells.

A baby's placenta and cord are usually just thrown away after birth. Connor's brother's cord will be drained first. It has blood-forming stem cells in it, like the ones in bone marrow. They can be transplanted into Connor to give him a working immune system.

Connor's transplant **donor** is his brother. Unrelated donors can sometimes be found. Frozen cord blood can be stored in case someone needs the stem cells later.

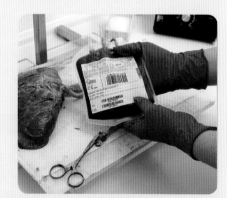

3 How will Connor's baby brother help to save his life?

4 Why do some parents get their baby's cord blood frozen?

Future cures?

Stem cells from cord blood can only make blood cells. But you have 300 sorts of cell in your body. The stem cells in 5-day-old embryos make them all.

In future it might be possible to inject the **embryonic stem cells** on the end of this pin into adults. They could replace dead heart muscle, or liver cells, so that transplants would not be needed. Stem cells are taken from embryos grown in dishes. But there are some big problems with transplanting embryonic stem cells into adult humans:

- As embryos develop, their stem cells sense where they are and what sort of cells to produce. It is hard to make them do this when they are transplanted into an adult.
- Patients need to take drugs to stop their immune systems attacking the new cells.
- Sometimes the stem cells won't stop dividing – so a **cancer** forms, which can kill.

Taking the stem cells also destroys the embryos which many people think is wrong.

5   What are the problems with using embryonic stem cells?

Growing your own

There are stem cells all over your body. Like bone marrow stem cells, they only make a few cell types each, but they might be more useful than cells from embryos. They could be used to grow whole new organs, or injected into damaged tissues to repair them.

Sasha is blind in one eye. The cells that cover it are damaged. They aren't see-through any more. Scientists used stem cells from her other eye to grow this new layer of cells in a dish. Doctors will use it to replace her damaged tissue.

Growing 3D organs is much more difficult. They contain several types of cell and have their own blood vessels and nerves. Scientists think it will eventually be possible to grow new organs – but very expensive.

6   Suggest two ways stem cells could help someone with a damaged liver.

7   What advice would you give to someone who says 'You don't need to look after your heart. Scientists will soon be able to grow new ones in a lab.'?

Get this

- Stem cells divide to make new tissues.
- Those in early embryos can form every type of cell.
- Other stem cells only make a few cell types.

Looking for life

Satellites can detect some types of life from space. The patches of dark green are **rainforests**. Their climates are hot, sunny and very wet so plants grow quickly all year round.

Paler green areas are cooler or drier like the UK. Grass grows best in places like this. Orange areas get much less rain, so only **desert** plants can grow there.

Oceans vary too. Most plants grow in the red, yellow and green areas of the water around the coasts.

All these areas provide different **habitats** for the plants and animals that live there.

1 What sort of climate does a rainforest need?

2 Why do so few plants grow in North Africa?

Life in the trees

This monkey has features that help it survive in a rainforest so it is **adapted** to this habitat.

Not much grows near the ground, so it lives in the treetops where there are leaves, fruit and seeds.

The monkey needs to leap across the gaps between trees. Its eyes face forward to judge distances accurately and its hands, feet and tail can grasp branches tightly.

Forest air is damp so even frogs can live in treetops. This flying frog eats insects. It uses suckers on its fingers and toes to climb, and the webs between its toes to glide from tree to tree.

3 Most rainforest animals live in the treetops. What makes this a good place to live?

4 Describe two adaptations that help animals hold on to branches.

5 How can rainforest animals move from tree to tree?

Desert life

Food and water are scarce in deserts. Most desert animals are **insects** or small **vertebrates**. They hide in cool burrows to avoid the highest temperatures.

Large mammals like camels and oryx endure the heat. They walk long distances to find food and can survive for months without drinking.

Water-holding frogs spend most of their lives underground. They grow fast when it rains, then fill their bladders with water and bury themselves in mud. They lie trapped underground for a year or more until it rains again. Then they pop out briefly to feed and breed. Native Australians used to dig them up and squeeze water from them to drink.

Large body heats up slowly

Moves around at night to feed

Concentrated urine and dry faeces

Does not sweat

Wide feet don't sink into sand

Stands in breezes at the tops of dunes

 6 Which adaptations help oryx save water?

7 Which help them stay cool?

Ice worlds

Antarctica is dark for four months of the year and mostly covered in snow. Few plants grow there, but microscopic plants called **plankton** fill the oceans that surround it.

These krill filter plankton from the water. There are more krill than any other species on Earth.

Huge colonies of penguins eat the krill, or fish that feed on them. There is less to eat in winter when plankton stop growing, but krill and penguins can survive for months without food. Their bodies shrink as they use up their energy stores.

Krill and fish can endure cold temperatures. They make antifreeze to stop their bodies icing up. Penguins stay warm thanks to their fat and waterproof feathers.

▲ Water-holding frog.

 8 What sorts of plants grow in the ocean?

9 Why do penguins lose weight in the winter?

10 How do fish and penguins cope with low temperatures?

Summing up

11 List two things that affect the plant life in a region.

12 Where is most food found in a rainforest?

13 What strategies can be used to survive in deserts?

Get this

- Earth has regions with different climates and different types of plants and animals.
- Animals have adaptations which help them to survive in their habitats.

3.2 Survival

Learn about
- Competition and adapting to change

Useful predators?

The tiny insects on this rose bush are aphids. They hatched just in time to suck sap from the buds. They reproduce rapidly and can cause a lot of damage.

Luckily, aphids have predators. These seven-spotted ladybirds can eat 100 aphids a day. Gardeners can order these predators from a pest control company.

 1   Draw the seven-spotted ladybird's food chain.

2   Why should gardeners welcome ladybirds?

Competition

In 2004, these foreign ladybirds crossed the English Channel. Since then their offspring have spread all over the UK. They eat more than other ladybirds and reproduce faster, so they are very successful.

When they run out of aphids they eat butterfly **larvae** and other species of ladybird.

 3   Explain why seven-spotted ladybirds might become less common.

Survival of the fittest?

Red squirrels used to live all over the UK, but now they are very rare. A few grey squirrels arrived here in the nineteenth century. They are immune to a virus that kills red squirrels and better at finding food – so more grey squirrels survive.

Many people want to protect red squirrels, so greys are trapped and killed.

 4   Why are grey squirrels becoming more common?

How do we decide... which species to protect?

The World Conservation Union lists **endangered species** and charities campaign to save them. Attractive animals like pandas get most help.

Living things depend on each other and their environment, so it is easier to protect an area than a single species. Very successful species – like rats – can be a nuisance. They get no protection. Pest control officers use poison to reduce their numbers.

5 Which would you choose to save – a rare frog or a koala?

Coping with change

It is hard to protect species from big changes in the environment like those caused by global warming. They affect some animals more than others.

In western Antarctica the air temperature has risen by 6 °C since 1950. Sea ice forms later now and melts earlier, but more snow falls.

Two species of penguins nest in the area:

- Adelie penguins are slow swimmers but they can hold their breath for a long time. They eat the krill that gather under sea ice.
- Chinstrap penguins can swim fast but can't hold their breath for long, so they feed in open water.

Chinstraps breed in spring but Adelies wait until summer when the snow has melted.

▲ Adelie penguin. ▲ Chinstrap penguin.

6 What is happening to the number of penguins?

7 Which species finds it harder to catch its food when there is less sea ice?

8 Adelies breed later than they used to. Why?

9 Adelie chicks grow less than they used to before winter comes again. Why do you think this is a problem?

| Year | Number of nests | |
	Adelie	Chinstrap
1990	11 554	223
1992	12 055	180
1994	11 052	205
1996	9228	234
1998	8315	186
2000	7160	325

Summing up

10 Why are red squirrels rarer than they were 100 years ago?

11 Red and grey squirrels produce about the same number of offspring. What could make more reds survive?

12 Is climate change a bad thing for every species?

13 When foreign insects enter the country they often leave their predators behind. What problems can this cause?

Get this

- Predators can be used to control pests.
- Animals compete for resources.
- Environmental changes can harm one species more than another.

Eat and be eaten

Camarra is on holiday in Africa. She sees herds of wild animals roaming freely. She'd like to get closer but knows that could be dangerous.

Learn about
● Food webs, photosynthesis and biomass

The animals she can see are all **herbivores**. Wildebeest, zebra and impala graze the grasses and giraffes pull leaves from the acacia trees.

But **carnivores** are hiding in the undergrowth, just waiting for a chance to catch their next meal. They could attack at any moment.

1 What do the herbivores eat?

2 Why do they need to be ready to run?

The herbivores have sharp senses and they can run fast. They are hard to catch. Many carnivores hunt in packs to improve their success.

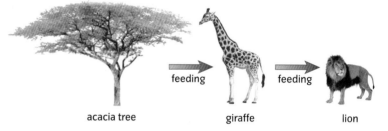

acacia tree feeding giraffe feeding lion

Lions are the top **predators** here, so they are the last link in the **food chain**. They prey on other carnivores as well as herbivores. This lion is feasting on its largest prey – a giraffe.

Vultures will pick the bones clean once the lions have had their fill. They are **scavengers**. They only eat animals that are already dead.

The **food web** on the right shows how the lion's food chains are linked.

3 Draw a food chain that includes a zebra.

4 Cheetahs are the fastest predators. Which animals do they catch?

5 Leopards and lions occasionally attack humans. Suppose they were all shot. What would happen to the number of herbivores?

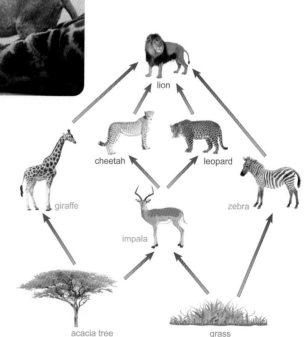

lion

cheetah leopard

giraffe zebra

impala

acacia tree grass

A gift from the Sun

Herbivores get their nutrients by consuming plants so they are **consumers**. Their numbers are limited by the amount of food they can find.

Plants make all their own nutrients by **photosynthesis**, using energy from sunlight, so they are producers. They only need to take in carbon dioxide, water and **mineral salts**.

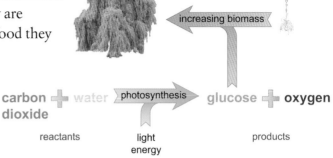

increasing biomass

carbon dioxide ➕ water —photosynthesis→ glucose ➕ **oxygen**

reactants — light energy — products

The amount of material in a plant (or any living creature) is called its **biomass**. The more plants there are, and the bigger they are, the more biomass there is for herbivores to feed on.

Grass grows fast in the rainy season, so there is plenty to eat. But growth slows down in the dry season. Grass plants store nutrients in their roots so they can push new leaves up when the rains return.

6 Why is it harder to find food in the dry season?

7 Can a zebra consume all the biomass in grass?

How do we know... where plant biomass comes from?

In the seventeenth century Jan Baptista van Helmont weighed a willow seedling and a tub of soil. Then he planted the seedling and watered it for 5 years. The willow gained 73 kg and the soil only lost a few grams, so he assumed the extra mass came from the water.

Later scientists proved that carbon from carbon dioxide, and minerals taken in with the water, also add to the biomass.

8 Why was the soil a few grams lighter after 5 years?

9 Few plants grow in the middle of the oceans. What could be missing from the water there?

The tree must be made of water!

Summing up

10 List three types of living thing that are linked by food chains.

11 Explain why food webs are more useful than food chains.

12 Life is 'a gift from the Sun'. Explain why.

13 What is biomass?

14 What is biomass made from?

15 What would happen to the grasslands if there were too many herbivores?

16 How do carnivores and scavengers differ?

Get this

- Food chains link to form food webs.
- Animals depend on the biomass plants make by photosynthesis, and this limits their total numbers.

Passing on energy

Predators

Cheetahs are the world's fastest land animals, but there aren't many of them. The further along a food chain you go, the fewer large animals there are.

Cheetahs need a large area of undeveloped land and plenty of prey. Their land is being taken for towns and farms so their numbers keep dropping.

Many wild carnivores are endangered.

 1 Look back at the food web on page 36. Why are there fewer lions than zebras?

Pyramids of number

Food chains show what each animal eats, but they don't show how many plants or animals there are.

A **pyramid of numbers** shows how *many* of each organism there are in a food chain. In the one on the right, a lot of grass at the base of the pyramid feeds a smaller number of impalas at the next stage and these provide food for an even smaller number of leopards.

But the pyramid is not always perfect. For example: when small animals like insects feed on trees the pyramid shape is spoiled.

 2 Draw a pyramid of numbers for this food chain. (Make each bar 1 cm long for each organism.)

     15   2   1

acacia trees → giraffes → lion

3 Show what this pyramid of numbers looks like. (Make each bar 1 cm long for each organism.)

     5   10   1

acacia trees → impalas → cheetah

Pass it on

Food chains and pyramids of numbers don't show the amount of energy passed from plants to predators.

glucose ➕ oxygen ⟩ respiration ➤ carbon ➕ water
dioxide

energy

Plants make nutrients by photosynthesis. But when impalas eat the grass they do not get all these nutrients. Plants use most of them for **respiration**.

Plant respiration happens all the time in every cell, just as it does in animals. The energy it releases keeps plants alive and lets them grow and reproduce.

 4 Why do plants need to respire as well as animals?

Impalas can only get the energy the plants used to grow new leaves. Parts of the leaves they can't digest pass out in their faeces – so they don't get it all. They use most of the nutrients in their food for respiration, just like the plants.

When a cheetah eats impalas, it only gets the energy the impalas stored in their muscles and fat while they were growing.

 5 What happens to most of the energy in the food impalas eat?

A better model

Pyramids of biomass show the mass of the living things at each level. This gets less at every step because most energy is not passed on. As a result, pyramids of biomass always have a pyramid shape.

 6 Draw a pyramid of biomass for this food chain.
(Use 1 mm for every 100 kg.)

acacia trees → giraffes → lion

(20 000 kg   (1500 kg)   (150 kg)
of leaves)

7 Convert this food chain into a pyramid of biomass.
(Use 1 mm for every 100 kg.)

grass plants → impala → cheetah

(10 000 kg)   (500 kg)   (50 kg)

Summing up

8 There are predators and prey in most parts of the world. Which are present in the highest numbers?

9 What is the same about every pyramid of biomass?

10 Why do big carnivores like lions need a large territory with plenty of vegetation?

Get this

- Pyramids of numbers show the number of organisms at each step in a food chain.
- Pyramids of biomass show their mass.
- Energy is lost at each step so the total biomass drops.

3.5 The cost of food

Learn about
- How we get our food
- Effects on the environment

Home grown

Samuel had porridge for breakfast, and bread and cheese at noon. Now he's tucking into hot soup made from home-grown vegetables.

300 years ago most people in the UK ate similar foods every day – mainly bread, porridge, dairy products, home-grown vegetables and fruit. Only the richest people ate a lot of meat.

Gemma's meal contains lots of meat, and food from all over the world – coffee from Ethiopia and salad from Spain. Coffee is brought here after it has grown. Salad crops will grow here, but it is cheaper to buy them from warmer countries. Ships, lorries and planes bring fresh fruits and vegetables from all over the world.

 1 Describe two differences between Samuel's and Gemma's meals.

2 Why can Gemma eat more foreign foods?

3 How might moving more food around by ship and air affect the environment?

Producing more crops

Food is cheap in the UK because farmers use chemicals to make more food grow on less land. They also use heated greenhouses to make plants from warmer countries grow well here.

Fertilisers increase plant growth by supplying extra minerals. **Herbicides** stop weeds growing, and **insecticides** stop insects eating the plants.

 4 Why is less land needed to grow crops now?

5 Why might a farmer use three chemicals on one crop?

Hidden costs

Most fertile land in the UK is used to grow food crops, or grass for cows and sheep. The chemicals used on crops have a big effect on our wildlife.

These fish died because fertilisers got into the river and made too many algae grow. Herbicides kill wildflowers and insecticides kill useful insects like bees.

 6 Why do farmers need to be careful with fertilisers?

Trouble in store

The first insecticides were powerful poisons. They are not used on crops any more, but they are still causing problems. They got washed into rivers, ran into the sea and were carried northwards by ocean currents.

Fish absorb them from sea water and store them in their fat. When seals eat fish the insecticide goes into their bodies. It gradually builds up because one seal eats a lot of fish. This is **bioaccumulation**.

Polar bears eat a lot of seals and get insecticides from each one, so their bodies contain even more of these poisons. Eventually the amount in their bodies is so high that they get sick and can die.

7 How did insecticides from fields in the UK get to the Arctic?

8 What is bioaccumulation?

Grow less – eat more

Gemma loves burgers but her brother is vegetarian. 'It's wasteful to eat beef,' he says. 'You could feed a lot of more people from the grain cows eat.' Pyramids of biomass show that he is right.

To grow enough meat for one burger a cow needs to eat the same amount of wheat as it takes to make six large loaves.

9 Why can you feed more vegetarians than meat-eaters from the same area of fertile land?

Summing up

10 List three sorts of chemicals that can be used to increase crop yields.

11 Why does bioaccumulation affect big carnivores like polar bears more than other species?

12 Grain can be used to make bread, alcohol, fuel or animal feed. Give three reasons why the demand for grain is growing.

13 Crops can't be grown on cold, windy hillsides but sheep can eat the grass that grows there. Do hillsides feed more vegetarians or meat-eaters?

insecticide accumulates

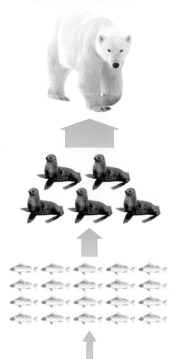

fish take in insecticide that gets washed into the sea and pass it on to their predators

Get this

- A greenhouse provides a warmer climate for crops from warm countries.
- Chemicals allow farms to produce more food. Some chemicals cause pollution and damage wildlife.
- The same amount of land usually feeds more vegetarians than meat-eaters.

3.6 Living for the future

Boom and bust

? 1 What killed off the reindeer?

In 1944, some reindeer were taken to an uninhabited island.

20 years later there were 6000 animals.

Then one winter most of them died.

Eventually, there were so many animals that the plants could not grow fast enough to feed them all.

More people, more problems

These newborn babies will all want good food, water, clothing, heating, electricity, transport and manufactured goods.

To avoid the same fate as the reindeer we need to make sure we don't run out of food, water, energy or materials. We also need to prevent our environment from becoming polluted with our waste products.

Giving growing populations everything they need without damaging the environment is called **sustainable development**.

? 2 All living things need food and water. What extra resources do we use?

3 Explain what sustainable development is.

Using more biomass

At the moment a lot of our energy and materials comes from fossil fuels like oil. As these run out we could replace them with fuels made from plants. This field of rape will be turned into **biodiesel** to save oil.

But growing **biofuels** leaves less land for food crops, so grasslands and forests are being cleared to make space. More than half the world's species live in forests. Removing trees damages food webs and makes species extinct, so it is not sustainable.

? 4 Why is it an advantage to replace oil with biomass?

5 What disadvantages do biofuels have?

Are we being greedy?

We can't use more biomass than plants can store. We already use more than a quarter of the total produced on land. Millions of other species share what's left.

If we could make plants grow faster, the cake would get bigger.

 6 Why do some people argue that we should use fewer plant products?

7 How could we get more without taking it from other animals?

Using small plants

Algae aren't popular. Some are toxic and they spoil lakes and ponds. But given the right conditions, algae absorb 10 times as much sunlight as land plants and grow much faster. They can use artificial light, recycled waste water and carbon dioxide from power stations. Humans can't eat them but they can be used to make biofuels and animal feed.

 8 List three advantages of growing algae instead of rape.

Future foods

Half of the world's population live in cities and the number is rising. Some scientists think we should develop high rise greenhouses and chicken farms for city centres. Then we could give more land back to nature.

Growing food indoors has lots of advantages. Plants grow faster because they aren't damaged by bad weather or pests, and less water is used because it can be recycled. Fewer pesticides are needed so there is less pollution. But energy is needed to provide extra light.

Summing up

9 How could you get lots of different crops to grow in a high rise greenhouse?

10 What would you miss if most food was produced in local greenhouses?

11 What would some of the disadvantages of high rise farming be?

Get this

- Species like humans with no predators can reproduce fast, use up their food supply and then die out.
- Sustainable development would stop this happening to humans and preserve other species.

Learn about
- Social behaviour

Eager to please

Jan is training his dog to do tricks.

The distant ancestors of dogs were wolves. Wolves are **social animals** because they live in groups. They also hunt together, so they need to cooperate. They adjust their behaviour to fit in with the pack.

Cats are descended from wild cats which hunt alone. They can be trained, but not as easily as dogs.

 1   What is the connection between a dog and a wolf?

2   Why are dogs easier to train than cats?

Running with the herd

This huge herd looks like a feast for the lion, but the predator will only get one of them – the youngest or the weakest.

Living together makes life easier for the prey. They can spend more time eating because there are more of them to look out for predators.

 3   Give two reasons why it's best for zebras to stay with the herd.

Warding off predators

When these musk oxen spot wolves or a polar bear they form a 'ring of horns' around the calves and females. They are rarely attacked.

Living together does have some drawbacks. Diseases spread easily, and the animals have to keep moving to find more food. When there are a lot of predators, the benefits outweigh the costs. But this strategy makes it easy for humans to shoot them.

 4   List two disadvantages of being part of a herd.

Knowing their place

This large male leads a group of chimpanzees. He gets extra food, the best sleeping place and more chances to mate.

The smaller chimpanzee is looking through his fur and picking out anything that shouldn't be there. This is called grooming.

The chimps in a troop recognise each other and remember where they fit in socially. Males have to fight for the top position but they also need to be popular, so they spend a lot of time socialising. They communicate using gestures, calls, facial expressions and body language, and by grooming each other.

5 What advantages do the highest ranking chimpanzees get?

6 Compare human and chimpanzee communication. What similarities and differences are there?

How do we know... about a chimp's social life?

Ethologists like Jane Goodall study how animals behave in their natural environment. Jane studied a troop of chimpanzees in Africa for 34 years.

Her findings changed people's ideas about the animals completely. She discovered they were not the simple fruit eaters people had imagined from looking at zoo animals. They fought, hunted smaller mammals, made tools, used medicinal plants and learned from each other.

7 What do ethologists specialise in?

8 Why were people surprised by Jane's findings?

Brainache

Q Whose memory is best – a chimp's or a university student's?

A When asked to remember where numbers were hidden on a computer screen, the chimps won every time.

Get this

- Social behaviours help species avoid predators or hunt more effectively.
- Animals that cooperate have to communicate with each other.
- In some species, high-ranking males have more offspring.

Summing up

9 What does it mean if an animal is social?

10 Why is it an advantage for predators to live in groups?

11 Why is it an advantage for a young chimpanzee to get on well with lots of other chimps?

Unnatural behaviour

When wild animals are kept in captivity their behaviour is affected by their new environment. This tiger walks backwards and forwards all day in his zoo enclosure. He is suffering from stress.

Wild cats roam over huge territories and have to work hard to find food. If they are trapped in small spaces, with nothing to do, their health suffers.

Modern zoos have bigger, more natural enclosures and they try to stop the animals getting bored.

 1 Why do carnivores suffer most in zoos?

Enriching lives

This polar bear lives in a modern zoo. There's no snow but the bears have a large enclosure with a cold salt water pool, an air-conditioned den and three smaller ponds. A weather machine makes wind, rain and fog to protect them from hot summers.

The bears' food is put out at different times, and hidden in different places.

But the main thing that stops them getting bored is taking part in a training programme every day. The keepers use rewards to train them to cooperate with zoo routines and move away from the display area while they put new food and toys out.

 2 Why is it important to make zoo enclosures match the animals' natural environments?

3 Wild bears spend hours trying to catch seals. What can zoos do to make mealtimes more of a challenge?

Useful behaviour

Jenny can't move. She relies on her monkey when she's at home by herself. The monkey can put music on, bring a sandwich from the fridge, comb Jenny's hair and take the lid off drinks for her. He is also fun to be with.

The monkey has been trained to do all these things. When he does the right thing, he gets lots of praise and sometimes a treat. Getting rewards makes him more likely to be helpful in future.

Most animals can learn new behaviours. If they can change their behaviour to get more food, or avoid harmful situations, they are more likely to survive.

4 When Jenny hits a switch on her control panel, a treat pops out of the box on her wheelchair. Why is it important to give the monkey treats?

5 Monkeys in the wild are sociable animals. How does this make it easier to train them?

How do we know... that rewards work?

A psychologist called Burrhus Skinner provided some of the first evidence. In one experiment he put pigeons in a box. They pecked the walls at random. If they pecked a lit button they got food. As time went by the pigeons pecked at the button more and more often.

6 Why did the pigeons get better at hitting the button?

7 Why was it important to use hungry pigeons?

Shaping behaviour

Jenny's monkey has had to learn to do complicated things. During training he was rewarded for each small step he took towards them. At first passing the sandwich got him a reward, then bringing it from the fridge, and so on. He soon learned to do the whole action.

 8 How would you train the monkey to open a cola bottle, put a straw in it and pass it to Jenny?

Brainache

Q Is it best to give a treat every time or just sometimes?

A Animals lose interest if they get a treat every time they do the right thing – random treats work better.

Get this

- Animals can learn to change their behaviour.
- They repeat behaviours that earn them rewards.

Summing up

9 The monkey sometimes dances around when Jenny takes him out. It makes people stop to say hello – which is nice. How can Jenny get him to do it every time?

10 What sort of behaviour shows that a zoo animal is bored?

11 How can zoos make animals more active?

Learn about
- Selective breeding

Problem pets

Kate's nose is runny and her eyes are red. There's something in the air and she's **allergic** to it. She gets these symptoms whenever she is near the cat.

No behaviour training can stop cats causing allergies. But a new breed of cat could help people like Kate. It doesn't make the substance that causes the allergy, because one of its **genes** is different. Genes shape the features of all living things.

1 List two symptoms an allergy can cause.

2 Why does Kate think she's allergic to the cat?

3 What is different about the new cats?

Tamed

All pet cats are descended from wild cats like this. The wild cats showed a lot of **variation**. Each cat had a unique combination of genes so they all looked different and behaved differently.

About 10 000 years ago the tamest ones started to live with humans.

4 What is variation?

5 List three differences between cats.

Nicer kittens

People have been selecting their favourite cats for thousands of years. They got the kittens they liked best by choosing their parents.

Suppose you wanted a small, plain kitten with big ears. You could let these cats mate. Then keep the kittens that are most like what you wanted, to be the next set of parents. This is **selective breeding**. If you did the same thing for many generations you might produce a new **breed** with all three features.

There are nearly 100 breeds of cat, but they all belong to the same **species**. Any pair can mate, and their offspring will also be able to reproduce.

6 List the steps involved in selective breeding.

7 What is the difference between a breed and a species?

Too much selection?

Wild cats compete for food and territory. In the wild, weak animals die before they can mate, so their genes disappear. But we protect pets, so weak ones could mate and pass on the health problems their genes caused.

Persian cats' genes make their faces very flat and this can make it hard for them to breathe. When selection goes too far it often produces unhealthy animals.

 8 Explain why some breeds of cat have health problems.

How do we decide... how far selection should go?

There are no laws to control selective breeding. Cats that belong to specific breeds are registered with a governing council. Show prizes are never given to animals with health problems. The council also refuses to register new breeds with distorted bodies like this Munchkin.

9 Why don't wild cats have distorted bodies like this?

10 How are breeders encouraged to produce healthy cats?

Accidental selection

One of this cat's genes doesn't work properly. It has made his heart weak. He will die soon from a sudden heart attack.

When breeders select features they can see, they can accidentally select ones they can't see at the same time – like faulty genes. Selective breeding has made faults more common in some breeds. Genetic tests can detect the most common problems.

 11 Why should breeders check for faulty genes or health problems before a cat is allowed to breed?

Summing up

12 Why is a cat similar to both its parents?

13 Why do members of a species show a lot of variation?

14 Explain why selective breeding takes a long time.

15 Why do pets inherit faulty genes more often than wild cats do?

16 Why should breeders check their cats' genes?

Get this

- Members of a species vary because they have different combinations of genes.
- Selective breeding produces animals with specific features by controlling which animals mate.
- It can cause health problems so it needs to be used responsibly.

Making improvements?

Glow babies

Four of these baby mice are not like the others. They glow green under ultraviolet (UV) light.

A jellyfish gene was added to their eggs. It went into the egg **nucleus** with their other genes. Adding genes to cells like this is **genetic engineering**.

Genetic engineering is tricky to carry out, but it has several advantages over selective breeding. You can add genes that aren't usually found in that species, and you don't have to wait for several generations.

 1 Whereabouts in the cell are genes kept?

2 What is different about genetically engineered cells?

Multiplying genes

The mouse egg cells were fertilised with normal sperm and began to multiply. They kept splitting in two to make all the cells in each embryo. Each new cell had a copy of the glow gene.

Glowing mice can be used for medical research. The glow can show what is happening inside their cells.

 3 How did the glow genes in the egg get into every cell?

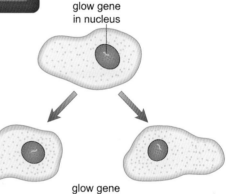

glow gene
in nucleus

glow gene
copied to every
new cell

Glowing plants

Glow genes can be put into plants too – and made to switch on and off.

In a month's time these seedlings will be short plants with tiny white flowers. The glow gene makes the flowers glow when they are short of water or when the soil is polluted.

Scientists hope to spray their seeds over hidden landmines. They will only glow where mines have polluted the soil, so they will show where they are.

NASA plans to grow the plants in a greenhouse on Mars. The glow will be videoed so their growth can be checked from Earth.

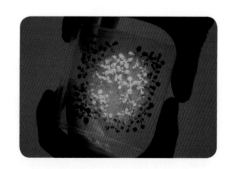

 4 Describe one way the glow gene could be used in plants.

Growing medicines

It takes skill and hard work to make new genes work in plants and animals. Bacteria are easier to use because their cells are simpler. They have no nucleus and their genes are loose in their **cytoplasm**. They also reproduce very rapidly.

Extra genes have been added to many bacteria to make them produce useful chemicals. One of these is human **insulin** for people with diabetes. Most people make insulin in their own bodies but people with diabetes can't.

The bacteria are grown in large tanks. The insulin has to be separated out before it can be used and this is an expensive process.

The insulin gene has also been added to this flowering plant. Its seeds fill with insulin.

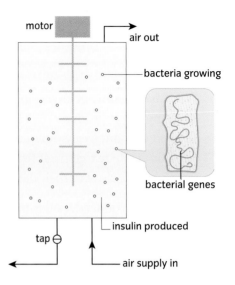

motor

air out

bacteria growing

bacterial genes

insulin produced

tap

air supply in

 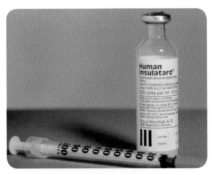

Some scientists worry about growing medicines in plants. Their pollen or seeds could contaminate food crops or cause other problems we can't predict.

 5   Why might it be better to grow insulin in a plant?

6   Give one argument against growing a medicine in plants.

Plants only produce seeds once a year but insulin is needed all the time. Now scientists have put the gene in cow and goat embryos.

When the animals grow up they will make insulin in their milk. But people won't actually drink the milk. The insulin will be separated out. Animals produce a lot of milk all year round, so the price of insulin could drop.

 7   Why might it be better to get insulin from cows?

Summing up

8   What does genetic engineering involve?

9   Cows that make medicines in their milk are usually kept indoors in large barns. Suggest why.

Get this

- Genes control what cells make and do.
- Genetic engineering puts extra genes in cells so they make useful substances. This is easiest with bacteria.

4.5 Choices

Cheap food?

When Sai's family goes shopping they buy free range eggs produced by chickens that are allowed to roam freely out of doors. They also buy humanely reared meat from animals raised in conditions close to their natural way of life.

Humanely produced food is more expensive. The cheapest food comes from animals raised in crowded indoor sheds. They have been selectively bred to grow fast. Keeping them indoors stops them running around and makes them put on weight faster.

Pigs reared outdoors spend the day socialising and searching for food.

1 Why do farmers raise pigs indoors?

2 How does this affect their behaviour?

How do we decide... whether farming is humane?

The RSPCA sets out criteria for the **ethical** treatment of farm animals. They produce detailed guidelines for each type of animal. Farms that follow the guidelines can put a 'freedom food' label on the meat to show why it is more expensive.

3 What does ethical farming involve?

4 Why is it important to label meat that has been produced ethically?

All farm animals deserve

Freedom from hunger and thirst
Freedom from discomfort
Freedom from pain, injury or disease
Freedom to express normal behaviour
Freedom from fear and distress

Better animals?

These cows have been selectively bred to give ten times as much milk as their ancestors would. They will give birth and start producing milk before they are two years old.

By milking time, each cow can be carrying 15 litres of milk, which makes it difficult for them to walk.

5 Why do dairy cattle produce far more milk than calves need?

6 What problems does that cause for the cows?

Better crops?

This is wheat – one of our main cereal crops. Its seeds are used to make bread and pasta.

Selective breeding has made the seeds bigger, but they contain less vitamins and minerals than older crops.

In the UK, vitamins, calcium and iron are added to bread and breakfast cereals to improve nutrition. In developing countries, many people lack vitamins and minerals. It would be cheaper to improve their crops than add these to their food.

7 What feature of wheat crops has selective breeding improved?

8 What negative effects has this had?

Useful improvements?

Rice is a common crop in developing countries. The golden rice shown here contains vitamins A and E. Half a bowl a day could stop undernourished children going blind. The rice plant produces extra vitamins because new genes have been added to it artificially. So it is a **genetically modified (GM) crop**.

9 What advantages does golden rice have?

10 Why is golden rice called a GM crop?

GM crops already grow in the US and many other countries. Most of the added genes make plants immune to pests, diseases or the chemicals used to kill weeds.

Many people are worried about GM crops because they think there might be risks to health or the environment. People who oppose GM crops in the UK have campaigned for many years to keep them out of the country. They think it best to wait for firm evidence that GM crops will do no harm.

11 What are the most common sorts of genes added to GM crops?

12 Why have so few GM plants been grown in the UK?

Get this

- Cheap meat can be produced by raising animals in crowded conditions.
- Selective breeding improves yields but can produce unhealthy animals and crops low in vitamins and minerals.
- GM crops can contain more nutrients and resist disease better, but many people are worried about them.

Life, death and beauty

Learn about
- Elements and compounds
- Using three different metals

Element of death

On 1 November 2006, ex-Russian spy Alexander Litvinenko met friends for lunch in London. He spent the night being sick. Days later his hair fell out. His liver started to fail. By the end of the month, Litvinenko was dead.

Detectives suspected murder. Scientists detected polonium in Litvinenko's urine. Polonium is poisonous. Just 0.000 000 000 007 g of it is enough to kill.

Polonium is a silver-grey solid at room temperature. Marie and Pierre Curie discovered it in 1898.

Polonium is an **element**. Each element is made of its own type of atom, which is unique to that element. You can't split an element into anything simpler. Each element has its own **symbol** – the symbol for polonium is Po. And every element has its own properties.

Every material in the world is made from one or more elements.

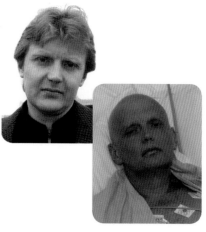

▲ Litvinenko before and after he was poisoned.

 1 Write down two things that are true of all elements.

2 Why do we use symbols to represent elements?

Element of beauty

Platinum is a silvery-white element. It's not poisonous. It's a metal, so it conducts electricity well. Platinum does not react with most other chemicals. It does not react with dilute acids. The symbol for platinum is Pt.

Platinum jewellery is shiny and popular. South Americans probably made the first platinum jewellery – including nose rings and pendants – around 2000 years ago.

Now, computer hard disks store information in layers of platinum and cobalt, another metal (symbol Co). Platinum in catalytic converters reduces pollution from cars.

▲ Ancient gold and platinum jewellery from South America.

 3 Give one property of platinum that is typical of most metals.

4 Give two properties of platinum that explain why it makes good jewellery.

▲ A computer hard disk.

Elements and compounds of life

Potassium is vital to life. It keeps your heart, kidneys and nerves working. A shortage of potassium makes people weak, confused and depressed, and can even cause heart attacks.

No one eats pure potassium – the element catches fire when it touches water. Instead, we eat compounds that contain potassium.

Eating too much ordinary table salt (sodium chloride) is harmful to health. So some people eat 'salt substitutes', which are a mixture of potassium chloride and sodium chloride. Foods like raisins, peanuts and bananas are rich in potassium compounds.

▲ Potassium reacting with water.

Compounds – remember them?

Compounds contain atoms of two or more elements joined together. The properties of compounds are often very different from the properties of the elements they are made from.

Property	Potassium, K (an element)	Chlorine, Cl (an element)	Potassium chloride, KCl (a compound)
State at room temperature	solid	gas	solid
Appearance	shiny when freshly cut	green	white crystals
Does it conduct electricity?	yes	no	not when solid
What happens when you add it to water?	It catches fire and zooms around on the surface of the water to make an alkaline solution and hydrogen gas.	It reacts to make hydrochloric acid and a solution that bleaches things.	It dissolves to make a colourless solution with a neutral pH.

 5 Use the table to give two differences between potassium (an element) and potassium chloride (a compound).

6 Which property of potassium tells you that it is probably a metal?

Get this

- Each element is made of its own type of atom.
- The uses of an element depend on its properties.
- The properties of compounds are different from those of the elements in them.

Summing up

7 Give one difference between an element and a compound.

8 Name the five elements mentioned on this spread, and give their symbols.

Learn about
- The periodic table
- Metals and non-metals

The periodic table

So far scientists have found at least 111 elements, each with its own unique properties and uses. How can we classify them usefully?

Scientists organise the elements by grouping together those with similar properties. The **periodic table** shows all the elements in their groups.

The periodic table is very useful to scientists. Knowing the position of an element in the periodic table helps a scientist to predict what an element is like and how it behaves.

1 Write down two facts about the periodic table.

2 Why is the periodic table useful?

Marvellous metals...and the rest

Most elements are **metals**. They are all together on the left of the stepped diagonal line. Metals have lots in common...but they are not all the same:

- Gold, copper and iron are just three of around 30 **transition metals**. They are shiny and conduct electricity well. Many transition metals react only slowly – or not at all – with water, air and acids. So they're used to make water pipes, electric cables and jewellery.
- Lithium, sodium and potassium are in the **alkali metal** group. They are shiny when freshly cut, and conduct electricity well. Alkali metals have much more exciting reactions than transition metals. You certainly couldn't make water pipes from them!

Unit 7 tells you more about metals.

The elements on the right of the stepped diagonal line are **non-metals**. They behave very differently from metals, for example they don't usually conduct electricity. All the elements that are normally gases are non-metals. Read the next few pages to find out more about non-metals.

3 Give two properties that are typical of all metals.

4 Give one difference between the transition metals and the alkali metals.

5 Give one property that is typical of non-metals.

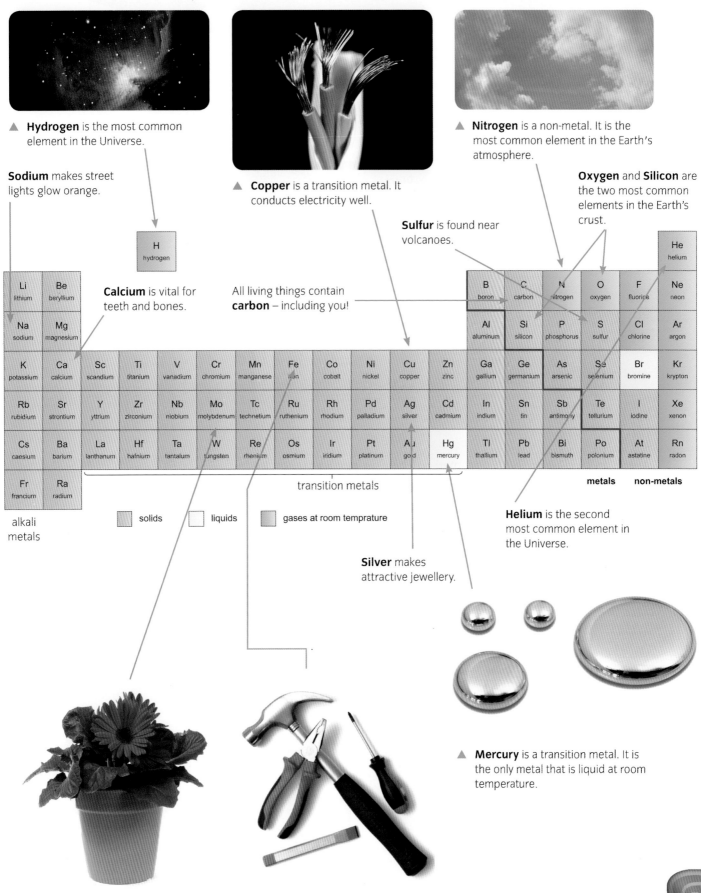

▲ **Hydrogen** is the most common element in the Universe.

Sodium makes street lights glow orange.

▲ **Copper** is a transition metal. It conducts electricity well.

▲ **Nitrogen** is a non-metal. It is the most common element in the Earth's atmosphere.

Oxygen and **Silicon** are the two most common elements in the Earth's crust.

Sulfur is found near volcanoes.

Calcium is vital for teeth and bones.

All living things contain **carbon** – including you!

																	He helium
H hydrogen																	
Li lithium	Be beryllium											B boron	C carbon	N nitrogen	O oxygen	F fluorine	Ne neon
Na sodium	Mg magnesium											Al aluminum	Si silicon	P phosphorus	S sulfur	Cl chlorine	Ar argon
K potassium	Ca calcium	Sc scandium	Ti titanium	V vanadium	Cr chromium	Mn manganese	Fe iron	Co cobalt	Ni nickel	Cu copper	Zn zinc	Ga gallium	Ge germanium	As arsenic	Se selenium	Br bromine	Kr krypton
Rb rubidium	Sr strontium	Y yttrium	Zr zirconium	Nb niobium	Mo molybdenum	Tc technetium	Ru ruthenium	Rh rhodium	Pd palladium	Ag silver	Cd cadmium	In indium	Sn tin	Sb antimony	Te tellurium	I iodine	Xe xenon
Cs caesium	Ba barium	La lanthanum	Hf hafnium	Ta tantalum	W tungsten	Re rhenium	Os osmium	Ir iridium	Pt platinum	Au gold	Hg mercury	Tl thallium	Pb lead	Bi bismuth	Po polonium	At astatine	Rn radon
Fr francium	Ra radium																

alkali metals

transition metals

metals   non-metals

solids   liquids   gases at room temprature

Helium is the second most common element in the Universe.

Silver makes attractive jewellery.

▲ **Mercury** is a transition metal. It is the only metal that is liquid at room temperature.

▲ **Molybdenum** is vital for plant growth.   ▲ Most metal things we use contain **iron**.

Learn about
- Noble gas properties
- Using noble gases

Who am I?
- I enter your lungs with every breath.
- You can't see, smell or taste me.
- I hide in the lights above your head.
- I don't do a lot – my Greek name means idle.
- My symbol? Ar.

And who am I?
- You can't live without my compounds…
- …but my violet vapour makes your eyes run and your lungs burn.
- My compounds lurk in milk and seaweed.
- My talents? Killing germs… and reacting!
- My symbol? Just I.

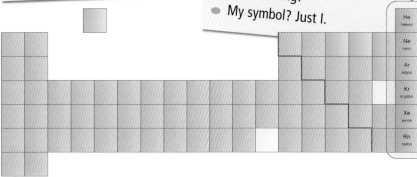

| He
helium |
| Ne
neon |
| Ar
argon |
| Kr
krypton |
| Xe
xenon |
| Rn
radon |

Argon and iodine are both non-metals. Their properties are totally different. So they're in different groups of the periodic table. Read on for more about argon and its group. Turn the page for more on iodine.

 1 Why are argon and iodine in different groups in the periodic table?

Noble gases everywhere

Argon is a **noble gas**, along with the elements helium, neon, krypton, xenon and radon. All the noble gases have similar properties. So they are in the same column – or **group** – of the periodic table.

The noble gas elements are very useful. Helium is in lasers that scan bar codes. Eye surgeons use krypton lasers to repair tears in the retina at the back of the eye.

 2 Name the periodic table group that includes the elements helium and xenon.

3 What property of argon means that it is used in double glazing?

4 What property of neon means that it is used in signs?

▲ Argon is in the gap between the two panes of glass in double glazing. Argon is a better insulator than air.

◄ The red signs contain neon gas. Neon glows red when high voltage electricity passes through it.

Noble gases: what are they like?

Many light bulbs contain argon. Argon doesn't react with the other materials in light bulbs – however hot they get. The other noble gases almost never react with other materials, too. They are **unreactive**. This is an important property of noble gases.

The table gives some properties of noble gases.

Noble gas	Colour	State at room temperature	Boiling point in °C	Reaction with oxygen	Reaction with hydrochloric acid
helium	colourless	gas	−269	no reaction	no reaction
neon	colourless	gas	−246	no reaction	no reaction
argon	colourless	gas	−186	no reaction	no reaction
krypton	colourless	gas	−152	no reaction	no reaction

5 Give three properties that are the same for all the noble gases in the table.

6 Which two columns in the table show that noble gases are unreactive?

7 Argon is in the air. What property does argon have in common with the other elements in the air, nitrogen and oxygen?

8 How do noble gas boiling points change as you go down the group?

▲ Xenon gas makes some car headlights blue.

Getting hold of noble gases

All the noble gas elements are found mixed with other gases in the atmosphere. Companies use special processes to separate them out from the air.

Helium is also found in natural gas under the land or sea. Companies in the USA and Algeria separate helium from the other gases in the mixture. The process is expensive, and costs are rising. So helium-filled balloons are getting more expensive.

9 Why is helium getting more expensive?

Summing up

10 Give three properties of the noble gases.

11 Explain why noble gases form very few compounds.

12 Give one use of a noble gas that relies on the fact that it is unreactive.

Get this

- Noble gases are unreactive.
- We use noble gases in lights, lasers and double glazing.
- Companies separate noble gases from the air.

Halogen Horror

Harry took a trip to a mythical world… The world of Halogen Horror. See his blog on the right.

Of course Halogen Horror doesn't really exist. But the story tells us a lot.

Halogen properties

The **halogens** are a group of elements in the periodic table. They have many similar properties. Some of their properties change gradually as you go down the group. Look at the table below.

Learn about
- Properties of halogens
- Using halogens and their compounds

http://www.halogenhorror.com

We entered a new world. A world where shiny black-grey rocks belch forth violet vapours. Where dark red rain falls from dark red clouds to fill dark red rivers. Where clouds of acrid green and yellow gases swirl around, killing every living thing. This was Halogen Horror.

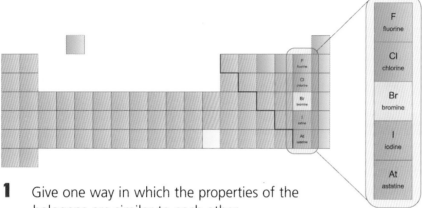

1 Give one way in which the properties of the halogens are similar to each other.

2 What happens to the darkness of the colour as you go down the halogens from fluorine to iodine?

3 Use the table to work out which element is in the rivers of Halogen Horror.

4 Use the table to work out which element is in the rocks of Halogen Horror.

5 Give one way in which the halogens are different from the noble gases.

Name of element	Colour	State at room temperature	Smell	Effect on living things
fluorine	yellow	gas	swimming pool	Very poisonous to all living things.
chlorine	green	gas	swimming pool	Kills bugs. Also kills people if breathed in. Used in chemical warfare and killed 5000 people in the First World War.
bromine	dark red	liquid	swimming pool	Kills bugs. Its vapour burns people's eyes and lungs.
iodine	shiny black	solid	swimming pool	Kills bugs. A useful antiseptic for humans. Its vapour irritates eyes and lungs.

Halogen compounds in your body

The halogens react very easily with other elements. They are very **reactive**. So the halogens make many compounds.

As elements, all halogens are poisonous. But the properties of their compounds are very different. In fact, we need some halogen compounds to survive.

- Hydrochloric acid – a chlorine compound – breaks down food in your stomach. It also helps destroy dangerous bacteria.
- Compounds of fluorine strengthen bones and teeth.
- Iodine compounds help control your body temperature.

6 Suggest why toothpaste contains compounds of fluorine.

Using halogens and their compounds

◄ Fluorine compounds in toothpaste prevent decay.

Getting hold of halogens

Because the halogens are very reactive, you never find halogens on their own. Instead, they're joined to other elements in compounds.

7 Why is chlorine never naturally found as an element on its own?

▲ Companies get chlorine from rock salt, sodium chloride.

Summing up

8 Write out the sentences below with the correct bold words.
The noble gases react with **many / few** other chemicals.
They are very **unreactive / reactive**. The halogens are very **unreactive / reactive**. They react easily with **many / few** chemicals.

9 Copy and complete the table.

Name of element	One use of this element or its compounds
fluorine	
chlorine	
bromine	
iodine	

Brainache

Q How do the names of halogens change in compounds?

A Chlori**n**e becomes chlori**d**e. So salt is sodium chlori**d**e.

▲ Some people put iodine solution on cuts to kill germs.

◄ Chlorine compounds make water safe to drink. They kill bacteria and viruses that spread disease.

▲ Seaweed contains iodine compounds.

Get this

- Halogens are very reactive.
- Our bodies need halogen compounds.
- Halogens make medicines and safe drinking water.

5.5 Four vital non-metals

What are you made

Jake has a mass of 50 kg. His body contains…

- enough hydrogen to fill his science classroom
- enough oxygen to fill his bedroom
- enough nitrogen to fill his school bag 85 times
- and enough carbon to make lots of pencils.

Jake's body also contains 0.5 kg of phosphorus and small amounts of other elements. The elements in Jake's body are not just mixed up. They are joined together in hundreds of different compounds.

Jake's blood is mainly water. Water is a compound of hydrogen and oxygen. Jake's nails are mainly keratin. Keratin is a compound. It is made of atoms of carbon, hydrogen, oxygen and nitrogen. There are also atoms of sulfur, which make keratin rigid and hard.

All Jake's body tissues and organs – including his skin, bones, brain and heart – are compounds made mainly of carbon, hydrogen, oxygen and nitrogen. Jake's pet dog and gecko contain compounds of these elements, too.
So do all the plants outside.

 1 Name four non-metal elements that are in all living things.

2 Give one difference between a mixture of hydrogen and oxygen and a compound of hydrogen and oxygen (water).

Compounds of carbon, hydrogen, oxygen and nitrogen are not just in living things. They're all around us. The properties of these four elements are very different, so they are not in the same group of the periodic table.

Learn about
- Elements in your body
- Using carbon, hydrogen, nitrogen and oxygen

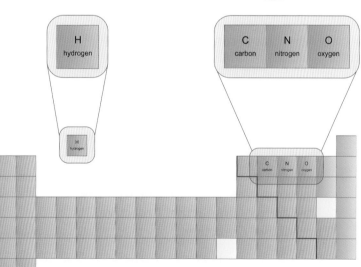

Carbon

There are huge amounts of carbon compounds in the Earth's crust. Limestone and chalk are different types of calcium carbonate. Oil and natural gas are mixtures of carbon-containing compounds.

Carbon is also found as an element. One form of carbon – diamond – is very hard. Diamond drills and cutting tools cut through almost anything. Another form of carbon – graphite – is softer. Graphite is a shiny dark-grey solid. It is mixed with clay in pencil 'leads'.

▲ Diamond.

3 Name two of the elements in the compound calcium carbonate.

4 Name two forms of carbon.

5 Give one property that is different for these two forms of carbon.

▲ Graphite.

Hydrogen, nitrogen and oxygen

On Earth, most hydrogen atoms are joined to oxygen atoms in the compound water. As an element, hydrogen is a gas at room temperature. Scientists are working out how best to use hydrogen as a fuel.

Nitrogen and oxygen are all around us, as elements, in the air. Companies separate them from the other gases in the air – and from each other.

When things burn, they are reacting with oxygen. We could not live without the oxygen we breathe in. Hospitals use oxygen in many treatments.

▲ Hydrogen fuels this motorbike.

Hospitals use liquid nitrogen to freeze blood. Liquid nitrogen also removes warts and verrucas. Nitrogen gas stops food going off – apples keep for two years in containers filled with nitrogen gas. Companies also use nitrogen gas to make hundreds of useful compounds. These include fabrics for clothes and fertilisers to make plants grow well.

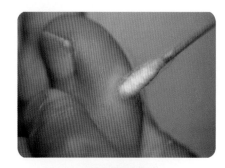

6 From where do companies get nitrogen and oxygen?

7 List two uses of oxygen.

8 List four uses of nitrogen.

Summing up

9 Name the four non-metal elements that are present in your body in the greatest amounts.

10 Where in the periodic table are the non-metals?

11 Why are carbon, hydrogen, oxygen and nitrogen in different groups of the periodic table?

12 Why do you think that carbon, hydrogen and oxygen are usually found joined to other elements in compounds?

Get this

- Your body is mainly compounds of carbon, hydrogen, oxygen and nitrogen.
- Hospital treatments use nitrogen and oxygen.
- Companies separate nitrogen and oxygen from the air.

Learn about
- Silicon and its compounds
- Semi-metals

Shanice is shopping. She buys hair conditioner and an iPod for herself. She picks up a pair of glasses for her dad. She ends up at the jewellers, gazing longingly at an amethyst ring.

Everything Shanice bought – or looked at – relies on silicon or its compounds.

Silicon chips

Can you imagine life without computers, televisions, mobile phones or iPods? These devices rely on microchips – electronic circuits made with tiny pieces of pure silicon. Silicon is a **semiconductor**. It conducts electricity less well than metals, but better than non-metals.

Solar panels, which generate electricity directly from sunlight, also contain pure silicon.

1 What is a semiconductor?
2 Name three devices that rely on semiconductors.

Silicon – metal or non-metal?

Silicon is a shiny dark-grey solid at room temperature. It is not bendy, but brittle – it smashes easily if you hit it with a hammer. Its brittleness makes it more like a non-metal than a metal. But silicon conducts electricity, which is what metals do. So scientists classify silicon as a **semi-metal**.

Germanium has similar properties to silicon. It is in the same group of the periodic table. There are other semi-metals, too. These are boron, arsenic, tellurium and antimony.

3 Give one property of silicon that's typical of metals.
4 Give one property of silicon that's typical of non-metals.
5 Explain why silicon is classified as a semi-metal.
6 Where in the periodic table are the semi-metals?

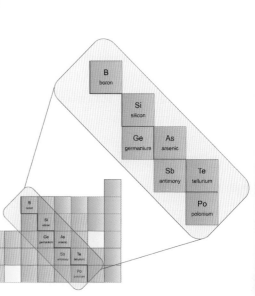

Silica and silicates everywhere

There's no shortage of silicon – it's the second most common element in the Earth's crust. Sand is silicon dioxide, and so is quartz. Ninety percent of the rocks in the Earth's crust are compounds of silicon.

Thousands of years ago humans used one form of quartz – flint – to make tools. Now pure quartz crystals keep accurate time in clocks and watches.

Sand reacts with limestone and sodium carbonate to make glass. It's been around for more than 6000 years. We still use it all the time.

 7   Name the two elements in the compound silicon dioxide.

Gemstones

Which of these jewels would you like to give – or receive – as a gift?

All gemstones are rare, hard and beautiful. That's why they're valuable. Amethyst and fire opal are mainly quartz, silicon dioxide. Tiny amounts of other elements give them different colours.

▲ Amethyst.

People have always been fascinated by gemstones. More than 1000 years ago the scientist Al-Biruni of Persia experimented with gemstones. He recorded his results in detail. The properties that Al-Biruni used to identify gemstones are still used by scientists today.

 8   Why are gemstones expensive? Give two reasons.

9   How do we know what techniques Al-Biruni used to identify gemstones?

▲ Fire opal.   ▲ Citrine.

Silicones

Do you condition your hair? Is there a waterproof seal round your shower or bath? If so, you use **silicones**.

Silicones are compounds. They contain long chains of silicon and oxygen atoms. Some silicones are slippery liquids. One of these is in hair conditioner. Other silicones are soft and rubbery. They repel water and don't catch fire. So they are used to waterproof tents and to make clothes for firefighters.

Silicone gel speeds up recovery from burns. It keeps water in the skin.

 10   Give one difference between silicon and silicones.

Summing up

11   Copy and complete the table.

Name	Use
silicon	
silicon dioxide	
silicones	

12   Give one difference between silicon and a typical non-metal.

Get this

- Silicon is a semi-metal.
- Silicon makes microchips.
- Silicon compounds make rocks, gemstones and hair conditioner.

The periodic table

Early ideas about elements

For thousands of years, scientists and thinkers thought about elements. They wanted to know about the simple substances that make up everything else.

More than 2000 years ago, a Greek philosopher created a theory. He said there were four elements – air, water, fire and earth. This was a popular theory in Europe for hundreds of years.

From the 1660s scientists started saying there were more elements. They looked for substances that did not break down into simpler substances in experiments.

Elements such as gold, silver, copper, carbon and sulfur are easy to find. But finding most elements is not easy because they are joined to other elements in compounds.

By 1860 scientists had agreed on about 60 elements. They wanted to organise the elements to help explain their properties. They also wanted a theory to help them predict other properties, or even to predict elements that no one had yet found.

? **1** Why was it difficult to find most elements?

2 Give two things that a science theory must be able to do.

Learn about
- Theories for organising elements

Order from chaos

In the 1700s, Manchester teacher John Dalton studied the results of experiments. He suggested that elements are made from atoms, and that the atoms of each element have a different mass. Later, the Italian scientist Cannizzaro worked out these masses.

Many scientists worked on finding patterns in the elements. But Russian scientist Dmitri Mendeleev was the one who, in 1869, first grouped the elements in the way we still use today.

Mendeleev made lots of small cards. On each card he wrote the name of an element, the mass of one of its atoms and its properties. He started arranging the cards like a game of patience.

Eventually he came up with an arrangement that worked. He put the elements in order of the mass of their atoms, from smallest to largest. He also grouped together elements with similar properties.

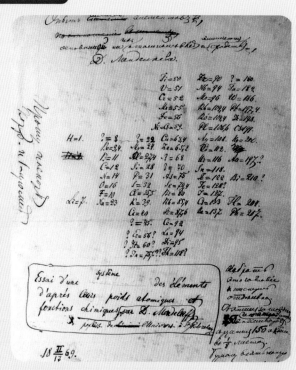

▲ Mendeleev's first periodic table.

Mendeleev wrote the arrangement on the back of an envelope. This was the first periodic table.

Mendeleev was confident in his theory. It explained what scientists knew about elements. He could use it to make predictions. Mendeleev was so confident his theory worked that he left gaps in his table where he was sure that an element should exist, even if it hadn't been discovered. He also used his table to predict the properties of these missing elements.

 3 Why did Mendeleev believe his theory was so good?

4 What did he predict using his theory?

Predictions come true

Just six years later, a French scientist found one of the missing elements. He discovered the element under aluminium, and called it gallium. The properties of gallium were those predicted by Mendeleev.

Swedish and German scientists soon discovered two more of Mendeleev's missing elements. Soon, most scientists accepted his periodic table.

Mendeleev didn't get everything right. He missed out a whole group – the noble gases – which hadn't been discovered at the time. But this didn't stop his periodic table becoming the foundation of modern chemistry.

 5 What helped persuade scientists to accept Mendeleev's theory?

6 You could call the periodic table an international invention. Why?

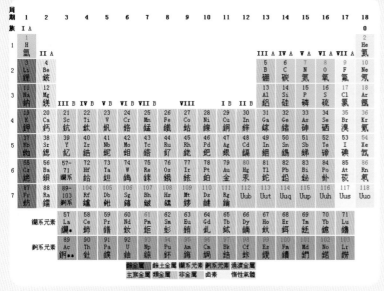

▲ Scientists all over the world use the periodic table. This one is from a Chinese textbook.

Brainache

Q Why's it called the periodic table?

A Because there is a repeating pattern of properties – just like the repeating pattern of menstrual periods.

Get this

● Mendeleev built on the work of earlier scientists to create the periodic table.

● He used it to predict undiscovered elements and their properties.

Gases – remember them?

Conor turns on a Bunsen burner. He can't light the gas. Soon the whole room smells bad. Why does the smell spread so quickly?

Gases consist of tiny particles. The particles are separate from each other, and they move around quickly. As they move around, they spread out, or **diffuse**.

Bunsen burner gas is mainly methane. This burns, but does not smell. Gas companies mix methanethiol with the methane. When methanethiol particles enter your nose, you detect a bad smell.

 1 Why do you think gas companies mix a smelly gas with methane?

The particles of every material are different. But they all consist of atoms. Some particles are only one atom. The particles of most materials contain more than one atom.

Noble gases

Helium is a gas at room temperature. Its particles are single helium atoms. Each atom moves around on its own. It is not attracted to any other atoms. So its atoms spread out easily.

You can picture a helium atom as a single sphere. A helium-filled balloon contains millions of these tiny spheres, all separate from each other.

Helium is in the noble gas group of elements, along with neon, argon, krypton and xenon (see page 58). All the noble gases exist as single atoms.

Oxygen

Oxygen is an element, like helium. But oxygen does not exist as single atoms. Its atoms go round in twos. These are **molecules** of oxygen. A molecule is a group of atoms that are tightly joined up. An oxygen molecule consists of two identical oxygen atoms.

Scientists use **formulae** to represent molecules. The formula of oxygen gas is O_2. The little '2' shows that there are two oxygen atoms in the molecule.

One Lego brick represents an oxygen atom. Two Lego bricks, joined together, represent an oxygen molecule.

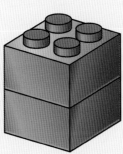

But atoms are actually more like spheres. So we often use spheres to represent atoms. Here, one sphere represents a single oxygen atom. Two spheres, joined together, show an oxygen molecule.

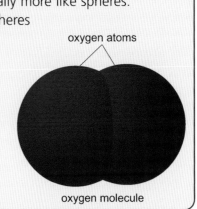

oxygen atoms

oxygen molecule

The atoms inside an oxygen molecule are strongly attracted to each other. But oxygen molecules are not attracted to other oxygen molecules. So, like helium, they easily spread out from each other.

It is difficult to split up molecules to get separate atoms. But they do split up in chemical reactions. So when oxygen reacts, its molecules split into two oxygen atoms. The atoms join to atoms of other elements to make compounds. For example, when carbon burns in oxygen, carbon and oxygen atoms join together. This makes a new substance – carbon dioxide.

 2 Nitrogen gas exists as molecules. Each molecule contains two nitrogen atoms. Write the formula of nitrogen gas.

carbon atom

oxygen atom

oxygen atom

carbon dioxide

Compounds

Many compounds exist as molecules. A lot of these compounds are gases or liquids. For example, a carbon dioxide molecule contains one carbon atom strongly joined to two oxygen atoms. Its formula is CO_2.

 3 How many atoms – in total – are in one carbon dioxide atom?

Summing up

4 Name two elements that exist as single atoms.

5 Chlorine gas exists as molecules of two atoms. Give the formula of chlorine gas.

6 Bunsen burner gas is mainly methane. Its formula is CH_4. How many carbon and hydrogen atoms are in one methane molecule?

Get this

- Gases diffuse because their particles are not attracted to each other.
- Most gases exist as molecules.
- The atoms in molecules are strongly joined together.

Our atmosphere today

The **atmosphere** is the layer of air that surrounds the Earth. It contains the gases that living things need, and helps to keep the Earth warm enough for life.

Air is a mixture of gases. The pie chart shows the percentages of the main gases in dry air. The total is not 100% because some of the numbers are rounded up. The air also contains tiny percentages of other gases, like neon and ozone (see page 73).

1 Name the two gases that make up most of the air.

2 Name three gases in the air that are elements.

3 Name one compound in the air.

4 Look at the pie chart. Which three gases exist as molecules?

5 Name one gas in the air that exists as single atoms.

Learn about

- The gases in the atmosphere
- How the atmosphere changes

Pie chart:
- 78% nitrogen, N_2
- 21% oxygen, O_2
- 1% argon, Ar
- 0.04% carbon dioxide, CO_2

Making our atmosphere

Our atmosphere has changed a lot since the Earth first formed.

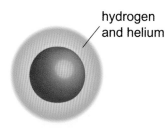

hydrogen and helium

▲ Some 4600 million years ago, the Earth formed from a ball of hot gases. Its first atmosphere was mainly hydrogen and helium – just like the rest of the Universe.

▲ The Earth cooled. Lots of volcanoes formed. They erupted and gave out lava, ash and gases (see page 90). The gases created an atmosphere made up of water vapour, carbon dioxide, ammonia and methane.

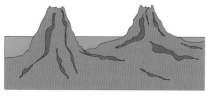

▲ The Earth cooled even more. Water vapour condensed from the air to make oceans.

▲ Plants first developed in oceans around 500 million years ago. They used some of the carbon dioxide for photosynthesis (see page 37) and put oxygen into the atmosphere. Some oxygen reacted with ammonia to make nitrogen. Some oxygen reacted with methane to make carbon dioxide. The rest of the oxygen stayed in the atmosphere and made life possible for animals.

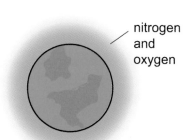

nitrogen and oxygen

▲ By 200 million years ago, the Earth's atmosphere was a mixture of mainly nitrogen and oxygen – just like it is today.

6 A hydrogen molecule is made up of two hydrogen atoms. Write down its formula.

7 The formula of ammonia is NH_3. How many nitrogen atoms are in one molecule of ammonia? How many hydrogen atoms?

8 The formula of methane is CH_4. Name the two elements in a methane molecule.

Humans change the atmosphere

Every time you travel by car or cook with gas you add carbon dioxide to the atmosphere. The amount of carbon dioxide in the atmosphere has increased hugely since 1900. Humans are responsible for most of this increase.

Cows make milk, beef . . . and methane gas. Rice growing produces methane gas, too. The more animal products and rice humans produce, the more methane goes into the atmosphere.

Carbon dioxide and methane are **greenhouse gases**. Greenhouse gases keep the Earth warm enough for life. But now their increasing amounts are warming it too much. Most scientists agree that global warming causes climate change. This will have massive impacts on life everywhere.

The plants of the world cannot use up all the extra carbon dioxide. When people clear forests to make room for crops and animals, even less carbon dioxide is removed from the atmosphere.

 9 Give three ways in which people increase the amount of greenhouse gases in the atmosphere.

Get this

- The atmosphere is a mixture of gases (mainly nitrogen and oxygen).
- Natural and human processes change the amounts of gases in the atmosphere.

Summing up

10 What is the atmosphere?

11 Where did the carbon dioxide in the atmosphere first come from?

12 Carbon dioxide is essential for life. So why do we see it as a problem?

Numbers of atoms matter

Entonox is a painkiller. It helps people after accidents. Women use it when giving birth. Entonox is a mixture of two gases.

One of the gases is oxygen. The other is a compound of nitrogen and oxygen.

 1 There are three different compounds that contain atoms of nitrogen and oxygen only. Use the data below to suggest which is in Entonox.

You know that the properties of a material depend on the atoms inside it and how these are joined. But that's not all. This example shows that numbers of atoms matter too.

Nitrogen monoxide, NO

- colourless gas
- no smell
- poisonous

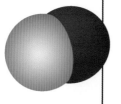

Dinitrogen oxide, N_2O

- colourless gas
- smells sweet
- relieves pain
- makes you feel relaxed
- not poisonous

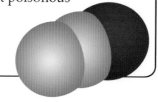

Nitrogen dioxide, NO_2

- reddish brown gas
- sharp, biting smell
- corrosive
- poisonous

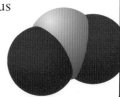

The properties of the three compounds above are very different. Only one of the compounds – dinitrogen oxide – relieves pain. It used to be called laughing gas – people inhaled it for fun to make them giggle and act silly.

 2 Suggest a second benefit of taking dinitrogen oxide after an accident.

3 Why is nitrogen dioxide not used as a painkiller?

Life or death: the difference an atom makes

Every cell in your body makes carbon dioxide as a waste product. The gas dissolves in your blood. Later, you breathe it out. Carbon dioxide is usually harmless.

Bill's gas heater wasn't working properly. It produced carbon monoxide gas. Bill breathed it in. His blood took carbon monoxide to his cells instead of oxygen. Before long, Bill was dead.

What's the difference between carbon monoxide and carbon dioxide? Just one atom! The formula of carbon dioxide is CO_2. Each molecule has one carbon atom joined to two oxygen atoms. The formula of carbon monoxide is CO.

 4 How many carbon and oxygen atoms are in one carbon monoxide molecule?

Oxygen and ozone

Oxygen usually exists as O_2 molecules. This is the oxygen our body cells need, and the oxygen in the air. But sometimes three oxygen atoms join together. This makes ozone, O_3. Oxygen and ozone have different properties.

carbon dioxide

carbon monoxide

Property	Oxygen	Ozone
state at room temperature	gas	gas
appearance	colourless	colourless
smell	none	like rain on wet ashes
effect on humans	vital to life	damages lungs
effect on ultraviolet light	none	high in the atmosphere, it stops some ultraviolet light getting from the Sun to Earth

 5 Give one difference between oxygen and ozone molecules.

6 Describe two properties that are the same for oxygen and ozone.

7 Too much ultraviolet light can cause skin cancer. What might happen if the amount of ozone in the atmosphere decreases?

Summing up

8 How many nitrogen atoms are there in a molecule of N_2O?

9 What is the difference between a carbon monoxide molecule and a carbon dioxide molecule?

10 Describe one property that is different for carbon monoxide and carbon dioxide.

11 Describe two properties that are different for oxygen and ozone.

12 Why do oxygen gas and ozone have different properties?

Brainache

Q Is nitrogen monoxide always poisonous?

A No. In tiny amounts, it's a vital body chemical. It carries messages to make your muscles relax at the right times.

Get this

- Properties of chemicals depend on the numbers of atoms in their molecules.

Magic material

What links the two pictures below?

All the pictures show things made from **polythene**. Polythene has useful properties. It is strong, tough and waterproof. It is an electrical insulator. Polythene can be flexible, too.

1 Give one use of polythene that relies on it being flexible.

2 Which properties of polythene mean it makes good shampoo containers?

Explaining polythene's properties

Polythene contains atoms of two elements – carbon and hydrogen. The atoms are joined together in long molecules. Each molecule is hundreds of atoms long. It is made of a chain of identical groups of atoms. Each group has one carbon atom and two hydrogen atoms.

These long chains make polythene strong and tough. Why? First, it is very hard to break a molecule apart. Second, the molecules are all tangled up, so it is difficult to separate them.

How do we picture... polythene molecules?

Model 1:

▲ One paper clip represents a –CH$_2$– group (one carbon atom joined to two hydrogen atoms). This chain shows many –CH$_2$– groups joined together. It represents part of a polythene molecule.

3 Suggest one advantage and one disadvantage of model 1.

Model 2:

▲ More often, scientists picture a polythene molecule like this. This shows part of one molecule.

4 Why is model 2 better than model 1?

5 Why is model 1 better than model 2?

More polymers

Polythene is a **polymer**. All polymers are made of very long molecules. There are thousands of polymers, each with its own properties and uses. Polystyrene makes cups and packaging. PVC makes pipes and clothes. Nylon makes clothes, too. Polymers are everywhere. They have revolutionised our lives since scientists first created polythene in 1933.

 6 Name three polymers. Give a use for each one.

7 Describe how your life would be different without polymers.

Natural polymers

Polythene, PVC and polystyrene are **synthetic polymers**. People and machines make synthetic polymers using chemical reactions in factories or science labs.

We also use **natural polymers**. Fibres like cotton, silk and wool are polymers. Their molecules contain thousands of atoms joined together in long chains. Natural polymers are made in chemical reactions in plants or animals.

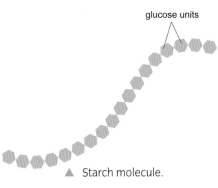

glucose units

 8 Name one synthetic polymer and two natural polymers.

▲ Starch molecule.

Eating polymers

You can't eat cotton or wool. But some natural polymers are vital for survival. Starch – in bread, potatoes, rice and pasta – is a natural polymer. Plants make starch molecules by joining together thousands of glucose molecules.

Proteins are natural polymers, too. Plants and animals make proteins by joining together thousands of amino acid molecules. Amino acids – and proteins – contain mainly carbon, hydrogen, oxygen and nitrogen atoms.

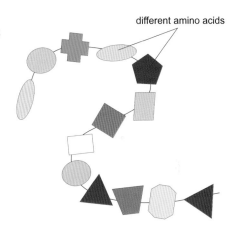

different amino acids

When you eat bread, your body breaks down its long starch molecules. You end up with small – and useful – glucose molecules. After eating beans, your body breaks down its long protein molecules to make amino acid molecules.

▲ Protein molecule.

 9 Name two polymers you must eat.

10 What does your body do to these polymers?

Get this

- Polymers are made of long chain molecules.
- Tangled chains make polymers strong.
- Polythene is a synthetic polymer.
- Starch and proteins are natural polymers.

Summing up

11 What is a polymer?

12 Copy and complete the table.

Polymer name	Natural or synthetic?	Uses
polythene		
cotton		
starch		

Learn about
- Reasons for solid properties

What are solids like?

Why don't solids flow like liquids and gases? Why don't they spread out? It's because of their atom arrangements. A lump of solid contains millions of atoms, all held together tightly in a regular pattern.

1 Give two properties of solids.

2 Look around you. Name three materials that are solid at room temperature.

Different types of solid

Solids are not all the same. Let's look at copper and a salt, sodium chloride.

Copper is a metal element. It makes thin, bendy sheets for roofs. It makes excellent electrical cables because it pulls into thin wires and conducts electricity well.

Sodium chloride is a salt. A salt is a compound that contains metal particles. Sodium chloride exists as white crystals. The crystals are brittle – they are hard, but easy to break.

The atom arrangements of these solids help to explain their properties.

Metals

Copper is strong because its atoms are strongly attracted to each other. The atoms are difficult to separate.

Copper is bendy because its atoms are arranged in layers. When you bend it, the layers slide over each other.

Like other metals, copper conducts heat well because its atoms are close together. Heating one end of a copper rod makes the atoms at that end vibrate more. These atoms bump into atoms nearby and make them vibrate more, too. Heat quickly transfers along the rod.

Copper conducts electricity when electrons carry the current between the layers of atoms.

All metals have atom arrangements that are similar to copper. So they all have similar properties.

▲ A copper roof.

▲ The atoms in copper metal.

Salts

Sodium chloride crystals contain sodium particles and chlorine particles. The particles are arranged alternately, in rows. They are held together tightly in a grid-like structure. The square grid explains why sodium chloride crystals are cube shaped.

▲ Sodium chloride crystals.

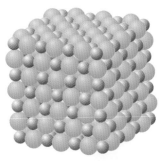

▲ The particles in a sodium chloride crystal.

Sodium chloride cannot bend because the particles cannot slide over each other. Sodium chloride breaks between its rows if you hit it with a hammer. But you can't separate sodium chloride into sodium and chlorine just by hitting it – you just make smaller lumps of sodium chloride.

Sodium chloride is not the only salt that forms crystals. There are many different crystal shapes, but they all have straight edges. The shape of a crystal depends on the way its particles are arranged. Most crystals are brittle and not bendy.

▲ Copper sulfate crystals.

3 Explain why metals are strong and bendy.

4 Explain why sodium chloride crystals are brittle and not bendy.

Changing solids

A scientist puts a piece of copper in a container without air. He heats the copper. Energy is transferred to the copper. At 1083 °C, the energy starts to break up the pattern of atoms. The copper is melting. Soon, all the copper is liquid. Its atoms still touch each other, but are no longer in a regular pattern.

▲ Iron sulfide crystals.

Most other metals – and most salts – also have high melting points.

Solids also change when they react with other chemicals. If you heat copper in oxygen gas, the copper does not melt. Instead, it joins with oxygen to make copper oxide. The reaction happens because copper atoms are more attracted to oxygen atoms than they are to each other. Copper atoms break out of their layers to join to oxygen atoms.

5 Give two ways of breaking up the pattern of atoms in a solid.

Summing up

6 Describe a property that is similar for a metal and a salt. Describe a property that is different for a metal and a salt.

7 Give reasons for the similarity and the difference.

Get this

- In most solids, the particles are arranged in regular patterns.
- The patterns break up when a solid melts or reacts.

6.6 Reduce, reuse, recycle

Learn about
- Recycling plastic bags
- Biodegradable bags

Reduce and reuse

If you shop in Ireland, China or Kenya you probably won't get a free plastic bag to carry your purchases home. Why?

On average, a person uses a plastic carrier bag for 12 minutes.

Millions of bags end up in the sea. Sea animals eat them, and die.

Plastic bags take hundreds of years to break down.

Plastics are made from oil. The process uses oil as an energy source, too. Oil is non-renewable.

Making plastics creates carbon dioxide, a greenhouse gas.

1 Give four benefits of banning plastic bags.

2 Shops in Modbury, England, do not give out free plastic bags. Would you like a plastic bag ban where you live? Explain why.

Environment organisations ask people to *reduce* and *reuse* all sorts of packaging. You can *reduce* your use of plastic water bottles by drinking tap water instead. You can *reuse* the same bags every time you go shopping.

3 Suggest one way you can reduce the amount of plastic packaging you use.

4 Suggest one thing you can reuse instead of throwing it away.

Recycle

If you can't reduce or reuse, then recycling is the next best thing. Most of the plastic we use can be recycled. Here's how:

- At home, people collect plastic waste. They put the waste out for recycling, or take it to a recycling bank.
- Lorries collect the plastic waste.
- At recycling factories, people separate different sorts of plastic by hand. They use symbols on the items to help them. For example PP is polypropylene and PS is polystyrene. Scientists are developing ways of sorting it mechanically.
- The different types of plastic are melted, separately. The liquids are poured into moulds to make new things.

Recycled plastic makes lots of useful things. This iPod case is made from recycled polycarbonate. The fleeces are made out of recycled plastic bottles.

5 Recycling companies ask people to crush plastic bottles. How do you think this reduces the fuel needed to transport them?

6 Suggest why scientists are developing machines to separate plastics.

7 Most plastic waste can be recycled. In the UK, only about 7% actually is. Suggest why.

New product for a purpose

Lots of people want more environmentally friendly packaging materials. Scientists are working hard to develop materials that meet this need.

They have discovered how to make a polythene-like polymer from cornstarch. Cornstarch comes from a plant, maize.

Cornstarch bags have many advantages. But the material is not perfect!

The bags only biodegrade if they are in the right conditions.

There is a world food shortage. We should use land to grow food, not bags.

Cornstarch bags are biodegradable. Microbes make them rot when the bags are buried in soil.

Farmers use tractors and fertilisers to grow maize. Making fertilisers and driving tractors both use fossil fuels.

My customers like cornstarch bags. They are transparent and flexible. They stop air and dirt getting to the food.

8 Explain the meaning of the word *biodegradable*.

9 Give one reason for using cornstarch bags instead of polythene bags.

10 Give one problem of cornstarch bags.

Summing up

11 Copy and complete the table.

	Polythene	Cornstarch
Properties		
What is it made from?		
Benefits of using this material to wrap food		
Problems of using this material to wrap food		

Get this

- Plastic for recycling is sorted, melted and made into new products.
- Cornstarch makes good biodegradable bags.

Metals

The same but different

Ben and Dan have new bikes. The bikes have metal frames.

 1 Write down two properties of metals that make them good for bicycle frames.

2 Write down two properties of metals that make them good for saucepans.

Metal elements have many similar properties. But there are differences, too.

Dan's bike frame is mainly aluminium. Ben's bike is mostly iron. A piece of iron is three times as heavy as a piece of aluminium the same size. So Dan's bike is lighter than Ben's. Dan transfers less energy than Ben when they cycle along together.

Aeroplanes are mainly metal, too. The lighter an aeroplane, the less fuel it needs. So aeroplanes contain lots of aluminium.

The bodies and engines of new cars contain more aluminium than older cars. So modern cars are lighter. Lighter cars need less energy to move. This means they use less fuel and produce smaller amounts of greenhouse gases.

 3 Explain why aeroplanes contain lots of aluminium.

Improving metal properties

Aeroplanes are not made of pure aluminium. It is too weak. Aluminium mixed with small amounts of other metals – like zinc, copper or magnesium – is much stronger.

A mixture of metals is an **alloy**. Alloys look and behave like metals. They are often harder or stronger than the individual metal elements that are in them. Scientists experiment with different mixtures to make an alloy with exactly the properties they want.

4 What is an alloy?

5 Most coins are alloys. Suggest why coin designers chose an alloy for £1 coins that is a different colour from the alloy in 10 pence pieces.

Melting point matters

Most metal elements and alloys melt at high temperatures. That's why they are solid at room temperature. But every metal element has a different **melting point**.

Metal	Melting point in °C
aluminium	660
iron	1535
mercury	– 39
tungsten	3410

 6 Copy and complete: At its melting point, a metal changes state from a solid to a _____.

7 Which metal in the table has the highest melting point?

8 A scientist heats up a solid metal. It melts at 660 °C. Which metal is it likely to be?

9 Which metal is liquid at room temperature (20 °C)?

The melting points of metals explain some of their uses. Tungsten has the highest melting point of all metals. When a thin tungsten wire conducts electricity, it gets very hot and gives out a bright light. But the wire doesn't melt. Glowing tungsten wires produce light in traditional light bulbs and some projector bulbs.

Mercury is an odd metal. It is liquid at room temperature. But it still conducts electricity. These two properties save lives in tip-over switches in electric heaters. When the heater is on, electricity flows through mercury in the tip-over switch. If the heater falls over, the mercury inside the tip-over switch moves. The circuit breaks and the heater switches off. This means the heater is unlikely to start a fire.

 10 Give two properties of tungsten that explain why it is used in projector bulbs.

11 Give two properties of mercury that explain why it is used in tip-over switches.

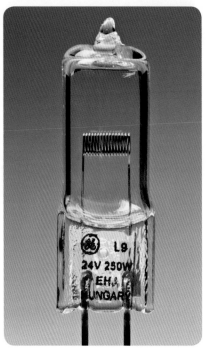

▲ Many projector bulbs have tungsten filaments.

▲ Mercury.

Summing up

12 Copy and complete the table.

Name of metal	One use of this metal	What property of the metal does this use rely on?
copper	To make electric cables.	It is a good conductor of electricity.
aluminium		
tungsten		
mercury		

13 What is the difference between a metal element and an alloy?

Get this

- Metal properties explain their uses.
- Alloys are mixtures of metals.

An exciting reaction

Do metals react with water? Not the ones we use most often. We'd have a problem if metal taps reacted with water, or if metal car bodies reacted with rain!

But some metals do react with water, and violently, too.

Emma drops a small piece of calcium into a beaker of water. It bubbles rapidly. After a while the bubbling stops. The piece of calcium seems to have disappeared.

The calcium has reacted with the water. The bubbles contained hydrogen gas.

 1 Give one sign that this is a chemical reaction.

2 How could Emma check that the gas is hydrogen?

More furious still

Calcium is not the only metal element that reacts with water. Other metals have even more exciting reactions.

Lithium whizzes round on the surface of a big bowl of water. It makes bubbles of hydrogen gas, like calcium. Sodium reacts even more quickly with water. Again, one of the products is hydrogen. The reaction of potassium and water is fast and furious. The whizzing potassium gets so hot that it sets fire to the hydrogen above it.

 3 Name the gas made when potassium reacts with water.

4 List the metals sodium, potassium and lithium in order of how vigorously they react with water. Start with the most vigorous reaction.

▲ Potassium reacting with water.

Not all metals react well with water...

Magnesium ribbon reacts with water. The reaction is so slow that you hardly notice it. Zinc does not react with cold water, but it does react with steam.

 5 Give one property of platinum that explains why it is used for pacemakers.

6 Describe one way in which the properties of calcium and platinum are different.

23 DECEMBER 2007

YESTERDAY, Chinese archaeologists raised the wreck of an 800-year-old ship from the depths of the South China Sea. The ship, which sank in heavy storms, was carrying exquisite treasures to sell overseas. The treasure includes gold, silver and tin pots, and 6000 copper coins. There's even a sailor's gold belt buckle and silver rings.

Why did the treasure survive under the sea for so long? It's because gold, silver, copper and tin don't react with water.

Metals that don't react with water are very useful. Copper makes excellent water pipes. Gold and silver rings are very attractive. And you can't damage them by washing your hands.

 7 Name five metals that don't react with water.

8 Give one use of gold that relies on it not reacting with water.

9 Give one use of copper that relies on it not reacting with water.

Summing up

10 List the metals below in order of how vigorously they react with water. Start with the metals that react most vigorously. Put the metals that don't react with water together at the end of the list.

Metals: sodium, silver, zinc, copper, calcium, potassium, magnesium, lithium, gold, platinum.

Get this

- Platinum, silver, gold and copper do not react with water.
- Potassium, sodium, lithium and calcium react vigorously with water to make hydrogen gas.

Metals and acids

Ring reactions

Sundara has a 22-carat gold ring. It is an alloy of three metals – gold, silver and copper. Sundara accidentally drops the ring in dilute hydrochloric acid. Nothing happens. She rinses it off and puts it back on her finger.

The ring survives because its metals do not react with dilute acids.

1   Name four metals that do not react with dilute acids.

More exciting reactions

Many metals do react with acids. Some of their reactions are more exciting than others.

How do we know... how vigorously metals react with acids?

Dan wants to compare how different metals react with hydrochloric acid. He puts small pieces of metal in test tubes of the acid. This is what he sees.

2   How can Dan make his experiment a fair test?

3   Give one sign showing that chemical reactions are going on.

4   List the metals in order of how vigorously they react. Start with the most vigorous.

5   Dan holds a lighted splint above the bubbles. It goes out with a squeaky pop. What is the gas in the bubbles?

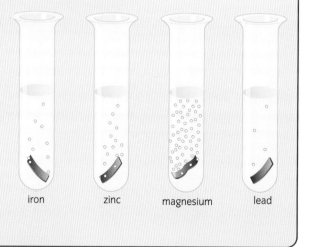

iron   zinc   magnesium   lead

What's going on?

During Dan's experiment, the piece of magnesium gets smaller. Eventually, it disappears. Only a colourless solution remains in the test tube.

The magnesium and hydrochloric acid have reacted to make hydrogen gas and magnesium chloride. The hydrogen gas leaves the test tubes in bubbles. The magnesium chloride dissolves in water, so you can't see it.

This word equation summarises the reaction:

magnesium + hydrochloric acid → magnesium chloride + hydrogen

 6 Name the reactants.

7 Name the products.

Magnesium chloride is a salt. Salts are compounds that contain metal atoms. You can make salts by reacting acids with metals or alkalis.

Zinc, iron and lead also react with hydrochloric acid. The reactions make hydrogen gas and salts.

8 What salt is made when zinc reacts with hydrochloric acid?

9 Copy and complete the word equation:
iron + hydrochloric acid → _____ + _____

A useful pattern

10 List these metals in order of how vigorously they react with dilute acids. Start with the most vigorous.
Metals: lead, copper, zinc, silver, magnesium, gold, iron.

11 Look at your answer to question 10 on page 83. Can you see any similarities in the patterns of metal reactions with water and with acids?

The pattern of metal reactions with acids is similar to the pattern of their reactions with water. Sodium and lithium react vigorously with water and violently with dilute acids. Next most vigorous are calcium and magnesium. Zinc, iron and lead react slowly (or not at all) with dilute acids and water. Silver and gold do not react.

The **reactivity series** describes this pattern of metal reactions. It lists the metals in order of how vigorously they react. The metals at the top have very vigorous reactions. They are the most reactive.
Going down the reactivity series, the metals get gradually less reactive. The metals at the bottom are unreactive.

potassium
sodium
lithium
calcium
magnesium
zinc
iron
lead
copper
silver
gold

▲ The reactivity series of metals.

Summing up

12 What is the reactivity series?

13 Which metal in the reactivity series is most reactive?

14 Predict what would happen if a scientist added potassium to a dilute acid.

15 Predict what would happen if you put a piece of copper in dilute acid.

Get this

- Some metals react with dilute acids to make hydrogen and a salt.
- The reactivity series lists metals in order of how vigorous their reactions are.

More on the reactivity series

Learn about
The reactivity series and:
- Burning metals
- The periodic table

Burning metals

The Second World War is raging. A bomber flies over a city. It drops 2000 bombs. The city is engulfed in hot white flames. Hundreds die.

The bomb casings were made of magnesium. Magnesium burns in air. Once the reaction starts, it is fast and furious. The magnesium is reacting with oxygen, so the product is magnesium oxide. This word equation summarises the reaction:

$$\text{magnesium} + \text{oxygen} \rightarrow \text{magnesium oxide}$$

Metals above magnesium in the reactivity series burn even more furiously. The picture shows burning sodium.

 1 Write an equation to summarise the burning reaction of sodium.

Small pieces of iron burn well. Many sparklers are tiny pieces of burning iron. But the reaction is less vigorous than magnesium's burning reaction. Silver and gold do not burn.

 2 List these metals in order of how vigorously they burn. Start with the metal that reacts most vigorously. Metals: Magnesium, sodium, iron, gold.

3 Compare your list with the reactivity series on page 85. In what ways are they similar?

◀ Burning sodium.

◀ Burning iron.

The pattern of reactions of metals with oxygen is similar to the patterns with water and acids. The reactivity series describes this pattern. The reactions of metals with oxygen provide more evidence for the reactivity series.

 4 Use the reactivity series on page 85 to predict two metals that burn less vigorously than magnesium.

5 Predict what a scientist would see if she tried to set fire to potassium.

Tallulah wants to know where nickel fits in the reactivity series. She tries burning a small piece of nickel. Nothing happens.

 6 Do you think nickel is above or below iron in the reactivity series? Explain why.

Tallulah decides to collect more evidence.

How do we know... where to put nickel in the reactivity series?

7 List the metals in the experiment in order of how quickly they react with hydrochloric acid. Start with the quickest reaction.

8 The evidence from this experiment suggests that nickel is between iron and lead in the reactivity series. Does this conclusion agree with the results of Tallulah's burning experiment?

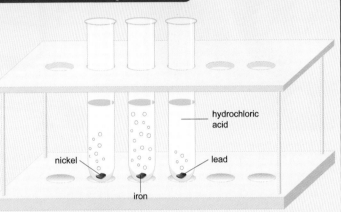

The reactivity series and the periodic table

The reactivity series fits in with another important scientific idea – the periodic table. The metals at the top of the reactivity series are in groups 1 and 2 of the periodic table. The unreactive metals are towards the middle of the periodic table. They are transition metals.

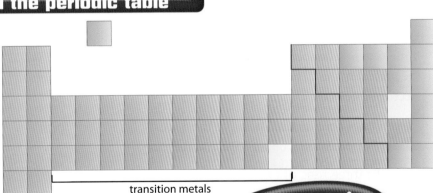

transition metals

 9 Platinum is a transition metal. Predict whether it is near the top or bottom of the reactivity series. Explain your prediction.

Get this

- Metals at the top of the reactivity series burn vigorously to make oxides.
- Metals at the bottom of the reactivity series do not burn.
- The position of a metal in the periodic table links to its position in the reactivity series.

Summing up

10 Name two metals that react vigorously with oxygen. Are these metals near the top or bottom of the reactivity series?

11 Predict what will happen if a scientist tries to burn lead.

12 Rubidium is in group 1 of the periodic table. Predict whether it is near the top or bottom of the reactivity series. Give a reason for your decision.

Learn about
- Using and extracting tin

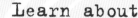

Terrific tin

Do you have fillings? Eat canned food? Use electronic gadgets? If you do, you rely on tin.

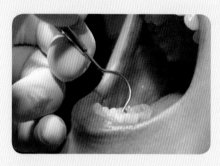

Every year, the world's people eat over 100 billion cans of food. Tin cans are mainly steel, an alloy of iron. But iron reacts with the acids in foods. So a steel food can would get holes in it and the food would go off. Coating the steel with a thin layer of tin prevents this problem. Tin is below iron in the reactivity series. It does not react with food acids, water or oxygen. The food is safe.

Every electronic gadget contains solder. Solder is an alloy of tin. It melts at low temperatures and conducts electricity. So solder is the perfect material for joining and holding together components in electronic devices.

Most fillings contain tin. The paste the dentist puts in your teeth is a mixture of tin, silver, copper, zinc and mercury.

1 Give three uses of tin.

2 Explain why steel food cans are coated with tin.

3 Name three metals that are more reactive than tin.

Getting hold of tin

You can't pick up lumps of tin from the ground. In the Earth's crust, most tin is joined to oxygen in a compound – tin oxide. Tin oxide is mixed with other compounds in tin ore rocks. Tin ore is not everywhere. Today, most tin comes from China, South America and South-east Asia.

There is also lots of tin ore in Cornwall. For thousands of years, miners dug the ore from the ground and extracted tin from it. But the process got too expensive. Tin from abroad was cheaper. In 1998 the last Cornish tin mine – South Crofty – was forced to close. Many people lost their jobs.

▲ Tin ore.

Then in 2006 the European Union banned lead from electronic devices. Lead is poisonous to humans and damages the environment. But lead – with tin – was one of the metals in solder. How can you make electronic devices without solder?

Scientists worked hard. They developed new types of solder. Most are mixtures of tin with copper or silver. All these new alloys contain more tin than the old type of solder.

So solder-making companies needed more tin. The price of tin tripled in five years. Is it worth mining Cornish tin once more?

A group of mining engineers believe it is. They recently re-opened South Crofty mine. They plan to use new technologies to mine and extract tin.

4 Name the two metals in old-fashioned solder.

5 Why did scientists develop new types of solder?

6 Suggest how banning lead from electronic devices changes people's lives.

Environmental costs

To get tin out of tin oxide, companies heat tin oxide with carbon. There is a chemical reaction. Carbon takes oxygen from tin oxide. The products are tin and carbon dioxide gas. Carbon dioxide is a greenhouse gas.

$$\text{tin oxide} + \text{carbon} \rightarrow \text{tin} + \text{carbon dioxide}$$

Some of the rock from tin mines is not useful. Companies used to dump this rock in huge spoil heaps. Few plants grow on spoil heaps – there is not much soil, and what there is may be contaminated with poisonous arsenic compounds.

7 Describe two possible environmental problems of tin mining.

Recycling tin

Do you recycle tin cans? What happens to them? First, the recycling company separates tin from the steel that it coats. Then the tin is used to make things…perhaps more tin cans. Recycling tin uses less energy – and produces less waste – than getting tin from the ground.

8 What are the benefits of recycling tin cans?

- Tin has many uses.
- Companies get tin from tin ore rocks.
- Mining tin can cause environmental problems.

The big one

Grace lives on the Caribbean island of Montserrat. She writes a diary.

12 August, 1995 More earthquakes. They say it's the volcano getting ready to erupt. Scary.	**March 2000** Volcano refuses to rest. Explosions last night. Newspaper: 'Showers of red hot rocks flung high, high into the sky. Spectacular and beautiful'. Wow!
21 August 1995 Sky hazy, dusty, yellow. Then black. Pitch black. And quiet. So quiet, but for the thunder. Everything now covered in ash. Dog terrified. Me too.	**March 2008** Volcano still active. Vulcanologists monitor it, day and night. They want no one to die in the next part of the eruption.
22 September 1995 Gran saw yesterday's eruption. Huge clouds of ash and steam – whoosh! – high into the sky. Gran evacuated. Us next?	
25 June 1997 This was it. The big one. Imagine. Hot rocks, ash and poisonous gases tumbling down the volcano – a massive pyroclastic flow. Hotter than boiling water. Faster than our car. Villages devastated. 19 dead. Thank goodness all the others evacuated.	

 1 Name a solid and a gas that came out of the volcano.

2 **Vulcanologists** are scientists. What do you think they study?

Where does lava come from?

The rocks under volcanoes are very hot. They melt to make **magma**. Magma collects under and inside volcanoes. It can come out of a volcano as liquid **lava**. But volcanoes can also fling out solid materials (like 'volcanic bombs' and ash), and gases (including steam, sulfur dioxide, chlorine and carbon dioxide).

 3 Name three compounds that come out of volcanoes as gases.

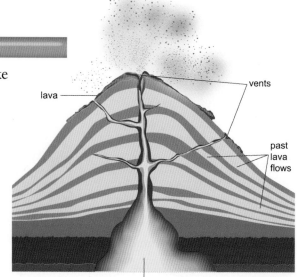

▶ Inside a volcano.

lava
vents
past lava flows
magma chamber

Vulcanologists save lives

It's impossible to know exactly when – or how – a volcano will erupt. But vulcanologists work hard to predict what a volcano will do next. They tell people when to evacuate their homes and get out of the way.

Vulcanologists make observations and measurements:

- Instruments measure earth movements – earthquakes – near volcanoes 24 hours a day. Different types of earthquake show different things happening inside the volcano.
- A satellite system (like SatNav) detects tiny movements of the Earth's surface. Tilt meters on the ground do the same. Changes in the readings show when magma is moving inside the volcano.
- Instruments detect how much sulfur dioxide is in the gases coming out of the volcano. Sudden increases show the volcano may be preparing to erupt.

The vulcanologists record their data carefully, and look for patterns. They use these patterns, and their knowledge of the past behaviour of the volcano, to predict what it might do next.

 4 Here are some tasks of a vulcanologist. Put them into the best order.

Tasks: make predictions, tell others of findings, make measurements, find patterns, record data.

5 No one can stop a volcano erupting. How do vulcanologists help prevent deaths from eruptions?

Volcanoes – not all bad!

Since 1500, volcanoes have killed around 200 000 people. But volcanoes are not all bad. Plants grow well in soil formed from volcanic rocks. Underground water gets very hot in volcanic areas. In Iceland, this hot water heats many homes. In other places, companies use underground hot water to generate electricity.

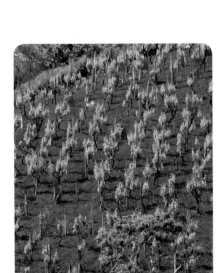

 6 Describe two benefits of volcanoes.

▲ Plants on the volcanic soil near Mount Etna, Italy.

Summing up

7 Explain where lava comes from.

8 What's the difference between magma and lava?

9 Describe how and why vulcanologists try to predict eruptions.

Get this

- Volcanoes give out lava, ash and gases.
- Vulcanologists collect and interpret data to predict eruptions.

Igneous rocks

Learn about
- Properties of igneous rocks
- How igneous rocks form

Granite

Gary is a TV chef. He needs a new kitchen worktop. He chooses between two materials – granite and wood.

Property	Granite (a type of rock)	Wood
Hardness	very, very hard cannot scratch with knife	soft scratches easily
Density in g/cm³	about 3	about 0.7
Effect of hot pan	none	may make a dark mark
Effect of water	none	may make it swell up

 1 Which material do you recommend to Gary? Explain why.

Gary goes for granite. His worktop is cut from a huge block of the rock. It is polished to make it shiny.

Granite consists of interlocking **crystals**, strongly joined together. The crystals are quite big – you can see them easily. Each crystal is made of a compound.

Elements and compounds that exist naturally are called **minerals**. Like most rocks, granite is a mixture of minerals. All its minerals are compounds. This sample contains four minerals.

Granite is an **igneous rock**. Igneous rocks are made when magma cools and solidifies.

 2 What is a mineral?
3 What is an igneous rock?
4 Name the change of state when liquid magma becomes solid rock.

More igneous rocks

Granite is not the only igneous rock. Another is basalt, which makes up much of the seabed. Igneous rocks are hard and strong. Most are also **non-porous** – water does not soak into them. This is because when they form there are no gaps between their interlocking crystals.

▲ Granite is a mixture of minerals: quartz (grey crystals), calcium feldspar (white crystals), biotite (black crystals) and potassium feldspar (pink crystals).

How do we know... if a rock is porous?

Take a small sample of rock. Drop water onto it. If the water soaks in quickly, the rock is porous. If water does not soak in, the rock is non-porous.

Q Are all igneous rocks non-porous?

A No. Pumice is full of holes. It is formed from lava that contains lots of gas.

 5 Gabbro is an igneous rock. List two properties that it is likely to have.

6 Explain why gabbro is non-porous.

Igneous rocks – not all the same

Basalt forms when runny lava pours out of volcanoes and cools quickly – often under the sea. As the lava cools down, crystals grow as the atoms arrange themselves in patterns. When all the atoms are arranged in crystals, there is no liquid lava left. It has become solid basalt.

Basalt's crystals are tiny. You need a hand lens to see them. The crystals are small because the lava cooled and solidified in just a few weeks.

Granite forms when liquid rock cools underground. The cooling takes much longer, so its atoms have more time to arrange themselves in patterns. This means the crystals grow bigger.

▲ The Giant's Causeway in Northern Ireland is made of basalt.

7 Which has smaller crystals, basalt or granite?

8 Why do you think that quick cooling makes small crystals form?

9 Most basalt forms from volcanoes under the sea, or when lava from land volcanoes enters the sea. Why do you think this is?

Summing up

10 Copy and complete these sentences.
Granite and basalt are _____ rocks. They are made when liquid rock _____ and solidifies. The slower the liquid rock cools, the _____ the crystals in the igneous rock. Most rocks are a mixture of minerals. A mineral is an _____ or compound that exists _____.

11 Andesite and gabbro are igneous rocks. The liquid that made andesite cooled quickly on the Earth's surface. The liquid that made gabbro cooled slowly, underground. Which of the two rocks has bigger crystals? Explain why.

Get this

- Igneous rocks are usually hard and strong.
- They form when magma or lava solidifies.
- The quicker magma or lava cools, the smaller the crystals in the rock.

Learn about
- Fossils and their rocks
- Sedimentary rocks

Fossil finds

It's the end of a hot, dusty day in Dikika, Ethiopia. Scientist Zeresenay Alemseged and his team have spent weeks looking for early human fossils. They've found fossilised otter bones and elephant bones. Surely humans could have lived here too?

Suddenly, someone spots a small fossil face in a dusty slope. It has a smooth brow and short canine teeth. The face is human.

For five years, Zeresenay studies the evidence. He works out that the skull, and other nearby bones, probably belonged to a three-year-old girl. He names her Selam. She almost certainly walked upright, like modern humans.

A geologist investigates the rocks around Selam. Evidence from the rocks shows that she lived by a river. Fossilised snails in nearby sandstone rock show that the river flowed into a lake with sandy beaches. Selam had plenty to eat and drink.

Many of Selam's fossilised bones were in a big lump of rock made from sand and pebbles. This shows that Selam probably died in a river flood. Fast-flowing water carried with it lots of pebbles and sand which quickly covered her

body, before predators could move her bones away. The geologist measures the age of the rock. It tells us that Selam died about 3 300 000 years ago. Her fossils are an important contribution to the story of humans.

Other fossils tell us about other ancient animals and plants. Their rocks tell us when they lived and what their environments were like… and so give clues about their lives.

?

1 Why did Zeresenay think early humans might have lived in Dikika?

2 How do we know when Selam died?

3 How did the geologist find out about Selam's environment?

What makes a fossil?

Fossils form like this. The process takes millions of years.

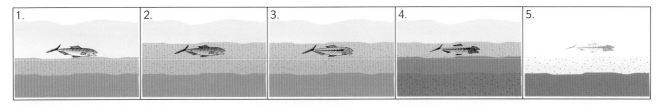

1. An animal or plant dies. It falls onto mud or sand.

2. More mud or sand buries the body.

3. Soft parts of the body rot away. Bones and teeth remain.

4. The mud or sand becomes rock. Hard minerals may replace the hard parts of the body.

5. Later, rocks around the fossil wear away. The fossil is exposed.

Sedimentary rocks

It's no good looking for fossils in igneous rocks. Animals and plants cannot live in the hot magma that made the rocks. Most fossils are found in **sedimentary rocks**.

Sedimentary rocks formed when pieces of sand, mud or dead plants and animals settled into layers and hardened into rock over millions of years. The layers are **strata**. Geologists use special techniques to measure their ages.

The picture shows four strata. The bottom layer formed first, so the fossils in this layer are the oldest. The fossils show which animals and plants were around when the rock was formed.

 4 Which of these strata was the last to form?

Sedimentary rock properties

Most sedimentary rocks are less hard than typical igneous rocks. They are usually porous.

The structure of sedimentary rock explains these properties. They are made of **grains**. The grains are held together less strongly than the crystals in igneous rocks. There are small spaces between the grains. Gases (like air) or liquids (like water) fill the spaces.

 5 Explain why most sedimentary rocks are porous, and igneous rocks are not.

Summing up

6 Why are most fossils found in sedimentary rocks?

7 What clues suggest that a rock is sedimentary?

8 Describe how fossils are formed.

Get this

- Fossils and their rocks tell us about ancient lives.
- Sedimentary rocks form in strata.

Sedimentary rocks

It takes millions of years to make sedimentary rocks. The process happens in stages.

Weathering

Weathering breaks up rocks into smaller pieces, called **sediments**. Their size varies from big boulders to microscopic clay particles.

Rocks break up in different ways:

- **Chemical weathering** happens when rock minerals like calcium carbonate react with acids in rainwater. Chemical weathering makes gravestone writing go blurry.
- **Biological weathering** happens when plant roots or animal actions break up rocks.
- **Freeze-thaw weathering** happens when water gets into rock cracks.
  - On cold nights, water freezes.
  - When water freezes, it expands.
  - The ice pushes against the sides of the crack. The crack gets bigger.
  - This happens again and again. The rock breaks.

Erosion

Many sediments are washed into streams and rivers. This washing away is **erosion**. The sediments are carried along by the water. They bash against each other, which makes them smaller and smoother. Some sediments travel in rivers for hundreds of years.

Making layers

When rivers reach the sea, they slow down. The tiny sediments suspended in the water drop to the bottom and settle in a layer. This is **sedimentation**. New layers settle on top of older layers. Eventually the sediments in the layers stick together. This is **cementation**. The layers become hard. They are now strata.

1 Write these stages in the best order:
Sedimentation, weathering, cementation, erosion.

2 Which type of weathering never happens in warm climates? Why?

3 What is erosion?

4 What happens in cementation?

Different sedimentary rocks

Different type of sediment make different types of rock. Each rock type has its own properties.

Learn about
- How sedimentary rocks form
- Types of sedimentary rock

▲ Freeze-thaw weathering.

▲ The sediments were laid down in strata to form this sedimentary rock.

Sandstone is very hard, so it makes a good building material. Its medium-sized grains are made of the mineral quartz (silicon dioxide). Other minerals cement the grains together.

Sandstone often contains fossils of animals that burrowed in the sand or lived in sea water above it.

Claystone and **mudstone** have tiny grains held together by pressure. They usually form under the sea, so they contain fossils of sea animals. The biggest ever carnivore fossil was found in claystone near Oxford. *Liopleurodon* lived in the sea. It was 25 m long with teeth twice as long as the teeth of *Tyrannosaurus rex*.

It is easy to mould wet clay into different shapes. Bricks and pottery are moulded from wet clay. They are then fired to make them hard.

Limestones are useful building materials. Incredibly, they are made from the remains of living things. Billions of dead animals and plants pile up on the seabed. Over millions of years, their remains make thick layers of limestone. The process still happens in places like the Bahamas. Limestones contain a huge variety of fossils.

▲ This building is built of sandstone.

 5 Sometimes, limestones with fossils are used to make the fronts of important buildings. Why are these rocks chosen for this?

▲ Fossils in limestone.

How do we know... that a rock is limestone?

Put a few drops of diluted hydrochloric acid onto the rock. If you see bubbles, the rock may be limestone.

There has been a chemical reaction. The equation is:

calcium carbonate + hydrochloric acid → calcium chloride + carbon dioxide + water

6 Use the equation to name a chemical in limestone.

7 Name the gas in the bubbles.

8 Acid rain sometimes attacks limestone. Why is this a problem?

Summing up

9 Copy and complete the table:

Rock	Property	Use
sandstone		
clay		
limestone		

Get this

- Weathering and erosion make sediments.
- Pressure and cementation turn sediments into rocks.
- Different sedimentary rocks have different properties.

Metamorphic rocks

Learn about
- How metamorphic rocks form
- Metamorphic rock properties

The same but different

Skilled craftspeople created these beautiful buildings from natural rock. The rocks of the two buildings look and feel very different. One is made of limestone, the other of marble.

▲ Bath Abbey is made of limestone.

▲ The Taj Mahal is made of marble.

But both types of rock are mainly one mineral – calcite. Calcite is the compound calcium carbonate ($CaCO_3$).

Property	Limestone	Marble
Colour	Whitish, grey or cream.	Usually white. Often has whirling streaks or spots of pale green, brown, red, blue or yellow.
Texture	Surface often rough. Tiny rounded grains. Gaps between the grains. Fossils often visible.	Surface usually smooth. Interlocking crystals, evenly sized. No gaps. Usually no fossils.
Reaction with diluted hydrochloric acid	Fizzes – makes carbon dioxide gas.	Fizzes – makes carbon dioxide gas.

1 Give two differences between limestone and marble.

2 Is limestone an igneous or sedimentary rock?

3 Name one product of the reaction of limestone with hydrochloric acid.

4 Why do limestone and marble react with acid in the same way?

Marble from limestone

Conditions are hostile beneath your feet. Just 15 km below the Earth's surface the temperature is a scorching 400 °C. The pressure at that depth is 4000 times greater than the surface pressure.

In some places, hot magma comes close to the surface. It heats up the rocks around it. Heat makes rocks change.

When limestone gets hot, its atoms arrange themselves in a new pattern. This makes big crystals which interlock tightly. A new rock has been made. Its name is marble.

magma chamber

layers of sedimentary rock

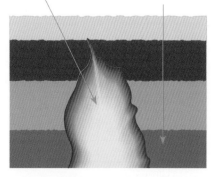

▲ Hot magma makes surrounding rocks change.

There is no chemical change when limestone makes marble. Both rocks are mainly calcite. White marble is pure calcite. Coloured marble has tiny amounts of other minerals mixed with the calcite. These show up as streaks or spots of other colours.

Marble can be translucent – it lets light through. So it sometimes seems to glow. Marble is soft enough to carve. It makes stunning sculptures. The Romans worked out how to use cement to stick marble to walls, and how to cover buildings with marble.

5 Explain why limestone and marble have different textures.

6 What makes marble streaky or spotty?

7 What properties of marble mean that it makes good sculptures?

Metamorphic rocks

Marble is a **metamorphic rock**. Metamorphic rocks form when heat, high pressure, or both, change igneous or sedimentary rocks. The rocks remain solid during the process. They do not get hot enough to melt.

8 In what ways are metamorphic rocks different from igneous and sedimentary rocks?

All igneous and sedimentary rocks can be changed into metamorphic rocks. So there are many different metamorphic rocks.

Slate is a dark grey metamorphic rock. It makes excellent roofing tiles because it easily splits into smooth, flat sheets.

Slate is made from mudstone. Mudstone is a sedimentary rock. It is a mixture of minerals. When new mountains form, high pressures underground squash mudstone. Water is squeezed out. There are chemical reactions between the different minerals in the mudstone. New crystals form and arrange themselves in layers. If the mudstone contains fossils, then so will the slate, but they will be squashed out of shape.

9 What makes mudstone change to become slate?

10 The squashed fossils in slate can tell you the directions of the pressures that squashed them. Use diagrams and words to explain how.

Summing up

11 Explain how marble and slate formed. Why are they called metamorphic rocks?

▲ A marble statue.

The rock cycle

How Science Works

Learn about
- Evidence for rock recycling
- The rock cycle

The story of our Earth

Imagine. It's 5000 million years ago. A great swirl of dust and gas comes together in space. It forms our Solar System. Most of the dust and gas ends up in the Sun. But some is left over. Gravity pulls this dust and gas into clumps. The clumps become planets. Our Earth is born.

Geologists investigate what happened next. They use rocks and the clues they hold to help tell the story of our Earth, and answer questions like these:

- What moves mountains?
- Why do oceans appear and disappear?
- How has our climate changed over the past few million years?

Piecing together the evidence

Two thousand years ago, the Greek scientist Strabo watched Mount Etna erupting. He saw hot lava spilling from the volcano. It cooled and hardened into solid rock.

A thousand years ago, Ibn Sina of Kazakhstan observed layers of rock. He wrote:

We see that some mountains appear to be piled up layer by layer and it is therefore likely that the clay from which they were formed was itself at one time arranged in layers. One layer was formed first and then at a different period a further layer was formed and piled upon the first, and so on.

Eight hundred years ago, the Chinese thinker Chu Hsi found fossilised seashells on mountain tops. He realised the shellfish once lived in the sea, and explained his observation by saying, 'Everything at the bottom came to be at the top.'

1 Which evidence shows that igneous rocks form from hot liquid rock?

2 Why did Ibn Sina think that sedimentary rocks are laid down in layers?

3 What evidence shows that some mountain top rocks were once under the sea?

Scientists continued to collect evidence about how rocks are made. In the 1700s, British geologist James Hutton thought about all the evidence. Eventually, he developed the theory of the **rock cycle**.

The rock cycle describes how rocks change and are recycled into new rocks over millions of years.

Of course, no one can see what's happening deep underground. Scientists work this out by looking at rocks formed long ago which have come to the surface.

The rock cycle

Weathering and erosion wear down mountains. The sediments make sedimentary rocks. Under the Earth's surface, high temperatures and pressures may turn sedimentary or igneous rocks into metamorphic rocks.

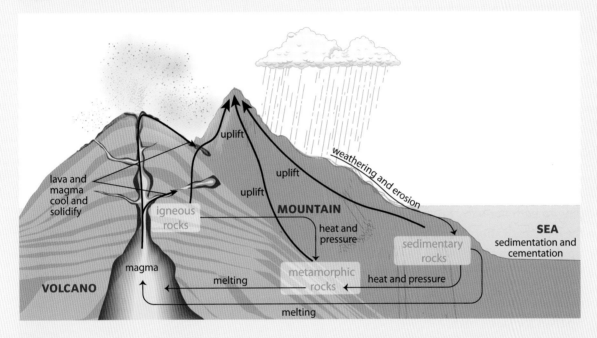

Some rocks sink deep under the Earth's surface. They get hot enough to melt and make magma. The magma is pushed upwards by pressure and convection. Some of the magma cools and solidifies underground. The rest of it comes out of volcanoes, and solidifies on the surface. Igneous rocks are made.

At any time, huge forces from inside the Earth may push rocks upwards to make mountains. This is called **uplift**. So any type of rock – sedimentary, metamorphic or igneous – may end up on a mountain top.

4 Write down, in order, three processes that make sedimentary rocks.

5 Describe how metamorphic rocks are made.

6 How do rocks from under the sea get to mountain tops?

7 Imagine the hundred million year journey of an atom around the rock cycle. Describe what happens to it on its journey.

Get this

- We can observe evidence for the rock cycle.
- In the rock cycle, rocks are recycled over millions of years.

Learn about
- Feeling hot and cold
- Heat and temperature
- Heat flow

Hot or cold?

Sita has just arrived from India. She thinks London feels very cold.

Magnus has just arrived from Iceland. He thinks London feels very hot.

1 Why do you think Sita feels cold?

2 Why do you think Magnus feels hot?

We clearly need a better way to judge hot and cold than how we feel.

Temperature tells us how hot something is. We use a **thermometer** to measure temperature.

Today we measure temperature in **degrees Celsius (°C)**. On this scale 0 °C is the temperature of pure melting ice and 100 °C is the temperature of steam from boiling water.

Heat and temperature

Megan is helping to bath her baby brother Jack. The temperature of the water in the baby bath should be about 38 °C. Her dad is doing the washing up downstairs. The sink has about the same amount of water as the bath but it is a lot hotter – about 50 °C.

Heat is a form of **energy**. It takes more energy to heat the water for the washing up than for Jack's bath.

3 Why does it need more energy to heat the water for the washing up?

How much energy?

The amount of energy needed to heat something depends on how much stuff is being heated as well as what temperature you want it to be.

Sometimes Jack uses the big bath in the bathroom. The water still needs to be at 38 °C. But there is much more water in this bath than in the baby bath so it needs more energy to heat it.

4 Why does it need a lot more energy to heat the water for the big bath?

The amount of energy needed to heat a substance depends on:

- how much is being heated
- what it is made of
- the temperature you want it to be.

Heat flow

Heat always flows from a hotter to a colder object. So the hotter object cools down and the cooler object warms up.

 5 Ben opens the fridge door. He says that the cold is coming out of the fridge. What is really happening?

Excited particles

When you heat something you transfer energy to its particles and they move faster. In a solid they **vibrate** more. In liquids and gases they move around faster. This means the temperature increases.

 6 Matt has just made some coffee. Its temperature is 90 °C. Zack's coffee has been cooling and is now at 60 °C. In which cup are the particles moving faster?

Why do you feel a freezing blast of air if you open a window on a cold night? It is *not* cold rushing in, but heat rushing out from your nice warm room.

▶ The particles in the warm air inside (red) are moving much faster than the ones in the cold air outside (blue).

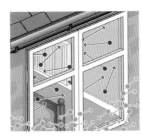

▼ They bump into them and transfer some energy to them.

▶ When the two meet, the warm air particles move more quickly amongst the cold air ones.

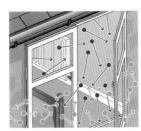

 7 Explain what happens in question 5, in terms of particles.

Summing up

8 Which of the following temperatures could refer to a hot summer's day in Great Britain?

20 °C   30 °C   50 °C   80 °C

9 Molly made herself a cup of tea but forgot to drink it. Why was it cold when she remembered it half an hour later?

10 Which requires more energy, heating 1 kg of water from 10 °C to 20 °C or 2 kg of water from 20 °C to 30 °C?

11 Susie holds a snowball in her bare hands. Her hands feel very cold! In which direction does the heat energy flow?

Get this

- Temperature is how hot something is.
- We measure temperature in degrees Celsius (°C).
- Heat makes the particles in an object move more, increasing the temperature.
- Heat energy always flows from a hotter to a colder object.

Conductors

The heat passes through the saucepan from the gas flame by **conduction**. Conduction is the way that heat is transferred in a solid.

Some solids conduct heat better than others.

The best conductors by far are metals. Copper is especially good at conducting heat. Expensive saucepans often have a copper bottom to quickly conduct heat through the base to the food inside.

 1 If you put a metal skewer through a jacket potato it cooks more quickly. Why?

Insulators

Many non-metals such as paper, cloth, wood and plastic are bad conductors of heat. We say they are **thermal insulators**.

 2 Why do saucepans often have wooden or plastic handles?

3 Explain why you might wrap a block of ice cream in paper to get it home without melting.

Air is also a very bad thermal conductor. Things like duvets and ski jackets keep us warm because they are made from a padded material that traps lots of air between its fibres. This makes it a very good insulator.

 4 Suggest why a duvet keeps you less warm if it has been flattened.

5 Explain why a bird ruffles its feathers when it is cold.

Losing heat

When Farah gets out of bed on a cold morning the bedroom carpet keeps her feet feeling warm, but the tiled bathroom floor soon makes them feel cold.

Carpet is a good thermal insulator. This means the heat energy stored in Farah's feet cannot escape so her feet stay warm.

 6 Why is carpet a good insulator?

The bathroom tiles are a good thermal conductor. This means the heat energy stored in Farah's feet is conducted away by the tiles, leaving her feet cold.

Remember! Feeling cold is always due to losing heat, not gaining cold.

Chain reaction!

We can explain conduction by thinking about what is happening to the particles in a solid.

- The particles in a solid are close together and arranged in a regular pattern. They vibrate on the spot.
- Heating the solid at one end transfers energy to the particles there and they vibrate more.
- They bump into nearby particles, transferring energy to them and making them vibrate more.
- These then bump into particles further along.
- In this way heat energy is quickly transferred to the other end of the solid.

 7 Air is a gas so its particles are spread out. Use this fact to explain why air is a bad conductor of heat.

Brainache

Q Why are some metals better conductors of heat than others?

A Their particles are closer together so they transfer energy more quickly.

How do we know... that moving particles transfer kinetic energy to heat?

James Joule was an English scientist who realised that kinetic (movement) energy is often transferred to heat. Even on his honeymoon he got his wife, Amelia, to measure the temperature of water at the bottom of a waterfall while he measured the temperature at the top.

8 What did Joule expect to find when he measured temperatures at the top and bottom of a waterfall?

Summing up

9 What passes from particle to particle when heat is conducted through a solid?

10 Why should I use a wooden spoon and not a metal one to stir a hot pan of soup?

11 Dan has a hot drink in a metal cup. Mia has hers in a polystyrene cup. Who has made the more sensible choice? Explain.

12 Suggest why lots of layers of clothes keep you warmer in winter than one thick garment.

Get this

- Heat energy is transferred in solids by conduction.
- Metals are very good thermal conductors.
- Bad conductors of heat, like air, are called insulators.

Convection

Learn about
- How heat energy is tranferred in liquids and gases
- Convection currents and their uses

A load of hot air

Have you ever wondered why smoke goes up a chimney? The smoke is hot. Hot air, as well as smoke, rises. The rising of warm air through colder air is called **convection**.

Warm spots on the ground heat the air above, and this warm air rises. Colder air falls towards the ground where it is heated. This movement of warm and cool air creates a **convection current**.

Birds, like this soaring bald eagle, use convection currents to rise and fall with very little effort. So do gliders which are aeroplanes without engines. An aeroplane tows a glider up into the sky. When they separate the glider uses convection currents, called **thermals**, to stay in the air.

 1   Why do houses lose most of their heat through their roofs?

Convection in liquids

We can use the special glass tube shown here to see how convection works in liquids. Some water at the top is coloured with a dye. The tube is then heated at one corner. The dye spreads around the tube as shown.

Why does this happen?

- The water near the flame gets hot and **expands** because the particles in the hot water move faster and get further apart.
- The water becomes less dense and so rises.
- Cooler, denser water moves in to take its place.
- This water gets heated, and so on.
- Soon the coloured dye has spread all around the tube and all the water is heated.

2   Why does the water become less dense as it expands?

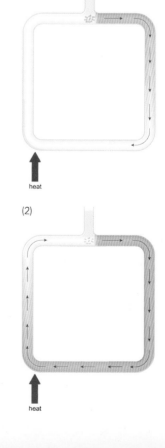

(1)

heat

(2)

heat

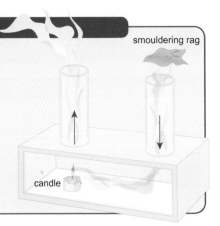

smouldering rag

How do we know... there are convection currents in air?

We can use this apparatus to see how convection works in gases. The smoke makes some of the air visible so that we can see where it goes.

3 Why do we use smoke?

4 Why does the smoke rise above the candle?

5 Explain how the convection current is formed.

candle

Using convection currents

We use convection currents a lot in everyday life. An electric kettle relies on convection currents to heat all the water inside it. The heating element in the kettle is at the bottom and this sets up a convection current. Modern kettles have the heater sealed in their base.

6 Draw a diagram showing how convection currents heat all the water inside an electric kettle.

In a refrigerator the freezing compartment is placed at the top so that convection currents keep the whole fridge cold.

7 Explain how convection currents keep the whole fridge cold.

Good convectors, poor conductors

Liquids and gases are poor conductors of heat. Wherever you heat a metal object the whole object will heat up. But if you heated a liquid in a test tube at the top, only the liquid at the top would boil.

8 Why are gases poor conductors of heat?

9 How are the particles arranged in liquids?
Use this to explain why liquids are bad conductors of heat.

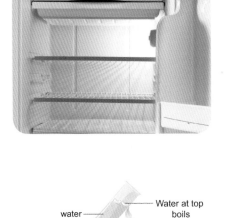

Water at top boils

water

ice cube

gauze to trap ice cube

hand touching bottom of test tube

Summing up

10 There are often warm air currents over motorways. Why?

11 Explain how all the water in a saucepan is heated by convection.

12 Suggest why the heating element of an electric kettle is not placed in the middle of the kettle.

13 Why would it be sensible to stay close to the floor if you were trapped in a smoke-filled room?

Get this

- Heat is transferred in liquids and gases by convection.
- The movement of warm and cold gas or liquid creates a convection current.
- Convection currents have lots of uses.

Learn about
- Infrared radiation

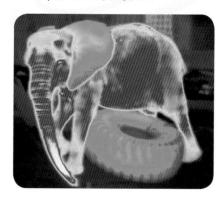

Looking at heat

This picture is a **thermogram** of an elephant playing with a tyre. It shows the temperature on their surfaces. The temperature scale is colour coded, from dark blue (coldest), through red to white (warmest).

 1 Which is warmer, the elephant or the tyre?

2 Which is the coolest part of the elephant?

We can 'see' the temperature of the elephant because hot objects give off **infrared radiation**.

Infrared radiation is a **wave**, like light. Both infrared radiation and light come from the Sun. You see the sunlight. You cannot see infrared radiation but you can feel it.

The Sun is a long way from Earth – about 150 million km away! There is a lot of empty space with no air particles in between. So the Sun's heat cannot reach Earth by conduction or convection.

 3 How do we know that infrared radiation does not reach Earth by conduction or convection?

Giving out infrared radiation

A hot object gives out, or **emits**, heat energy as radiation. The hotter the object the more energy it radiates. We give out infrared radiation too!

An electric fire gets hot enough to emit red light as well. An electric iron (for ironing clothes) is not hot enough to radiate visible light but it does radiate infrared.

If you put your hand near the fire or iron, you can feel the radiation from it – but don't touch it!

 4 Suggest why you are less likely to burn yourself on an electric fire than an iron although the fire is hotter.

Thermal imaging cameras detect infrared radiation given out by warm objects and produce thermograms.

They are used in medicine because diseased tissue is often warmer than healthy tissue. This thermogram shows arthritis in the joints of one hand.

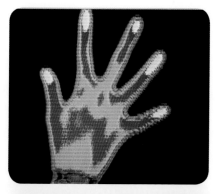

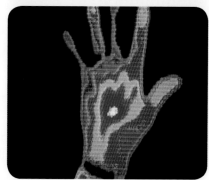

5 Which hand has arthritis?

Molly is wrapped in a sheet of aluminium foil. She gives out infrared radiation. The shiny aluminium **reflects** the radiation back towards her body so it doesn't escape. This helps to keep her warm.

Shiny, light-coloured surfaces reflect heat radiation just as they reflect light. They are bad at giving it out. Matt, dark-coloured surfaces are very good at giving out, or emitting, heat radiation.

 6 Suggest why saucepans usually have shiny surfaces.

How can we show... that shiny surfaces emit less radiation?

Both teapots in this diagram are made of the same metal. Just 5 minutes after the tea is made, the tea from the dull black one is cooler than the tea from the shiny silver one.

7 How would you investigate whether this is due to the colours of the teapots? What would you keep the same to make this a fair test?

80°C   85°C

Taking in infrared radiation

Dark colours and dull surfaces take in, or **absorb**, radiation very well. Winter coats are often dark and dull but will absorb any slight warmth from the Sun. Light-coloured shiny surfaces are bad at absorbing radiation; they reflect it away.

 8 Why are houses in hot countries often painted white?

Brainache

Q Why don't we paint our central heating radiators black?

A 'Radiators' actually heat a room mainly by convection.

Get this

- Infrared radiation does not need particles to transfer heat energy from one place to another.
- Infrared is a wave, like light.
- Shiny light surfaces are bad at emitting and absorbing infrared; they reflect it.
- Matt black surfaces are good at emitting and absorbing infrared.

Summing up

9 How can a thermal imaging camera produce a picture in the dark?

10 Explain how the Sun's heat reaches us.

11 Why do firefighters sometimes wear bright shiny suits?

12 When you put food under a hot grill, the heat is transferred to it by radiation. How do you know heat does not reach it by conduction or convection?

Conserving energy

Energy flow

Objects give out and take in heat energy all the time. The hotter the object the more heat energy it gives out.

1 Why is Kate giving out more heat energy than she receives?

2 Why is Ali gaining more heat energy than he gives out?

Heat energy moves from a warm place to a colder one because of the difference in temperature between them. The energy transfer is always from hot to cold.

Reducing energy transfer

Transfer of heat energy can happen by conduction, convection and radiation, and often all three together.

A vacuum (Thermos) flask is designed to keep a hot drink hot or ice cream cold. It reduces energy transfer to or from the air outside by conduction, convection and radiation.

- A **vacuum** has no particles of any kind in it – this reduces heat transfer by conduction and convection.
- The shiny silver surfaces reflect infrared radiation.
- The stopper is made of an insulator so heat energy is not transferred by conduction. It also stops convection transferring energy to or from the room.

Wearing a ski jacket would help to keep Kate warm.

 3 Does the ski jacket reduce heat loss mainly by conduction, convection or radiation? Explain your answer.

Emperor penguins survive Antarctic winters in temperatures of −30 °C and below. One of the ways they keep warm is to huddle together. 6000 or so penguins can huddle very closely together taking turns to be on the outside of the huge crowd.

 4 Why does huddling together cut down heat loss?

Conserving energy

You might lose energy of the sort you want, or from the place you want it to be, but it is never actually lost to the world. If energy from your hot drink moves to the air above it the energy still exists. Unfortunately the small amount of energy from your hot drink gets so spread out in the air that it is no use to anyone.

Learn about
- Reducing heat loss
- Conserving energy
- Sankey diagrams

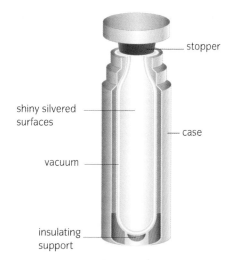

stopper

shiny silvered surfaces

case

vacuum

insulating support

A light bulb transfers energy from electricity to light. But the bulb gets hot, so some electrical energy is also transferred to heat, which transfers to the air. This is **wasted energy**. It cannot be used again.

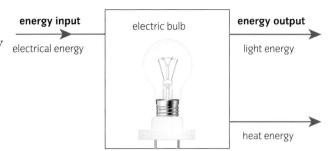

energy input
electrical energy

electric bulb

energy output
light energy

heat energy

 5 Why can't the heat energy from the light bulb be used again?

total energy input = total energy output

We measure energy in **joules (J)**.

For every 100 J of energy that go into the bulb, 90 J change to heat and only 10 J change to light. But 90 + 10 = 100 so no energy is lost.

Sankey diagrams

Sankey diagrams show all the energy transfers taking place in a process. The thicker the arrow, the greater the amount of energy transferred. The Sankey diagram for an electric lamp shows that most of the electrical energy is changed to heat rather than light.

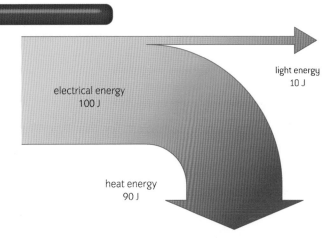

electrical energy
100 J

light energy
10 J

heat energy
90 J

For every 100 J of electrical energy supplied, an energy-saving light bulb transfers about 80 J of energy as light and the rest as heat to the surroundings.

 6 Draw a Sankey diagram for an energy-saving light bulb.

7 How much more energy does the energy-saving light bulb transfer to light compared with an old-style bulb?

Get this

- Most heat transfer happens by conduction, convection and radiation and often all three.
- Energy cannot be gained or lost. It can only be changed from one form to another.
- Sankey diagrams show the energy transfers in a process.

Summing up

8 What is the only form of heat transfer that can cross a vacuum?

9 Why should we use energy-saving light bulbs?

10 A portable CD player transfers 50 J of energy to sound and 300 J to heat. When 700 J of electrical energy are supplied how much does it transfer to sound?

11 Draw a Sankey diagram for the CD player in question 10.

Space shuttle

What is a space shuttle?

Space shuttles were the world's first reuseable spacecraft. They are launched by a rocket but land like a conventional aeroplane.

Problem solving

This was a completely new idea. A huge amount of research was needed. Rocket technology was quite advanced but bringing the shuttle back safely to Earth was a new problem.

Scientists realised that as the shuttle re-entered Earth's atmosphere it would hit air particles at a speed of about 28 000 km/h. The huge friction force created would heat the shuttle to a temperature of about 1650 °C.

1 What causes the friction force?

2 Why is this friction a problem for the astronauts inside the space shuttle?

3 Meteors are rocks that approach Earth at high speed from space. On entering Earth's atmosphere they break up and give off light. Explain why.

Scientists had to develop special insulating materials to prevent the shuttle burning up during **re-entry**. These materials have to absorb large quantities of heat without increasing their temperature very much.

4 How does the heat energy produced reach the inside of the shuttle? Choose from conduction, convection or radiation.

Silica, an excellent insulator, is used to make tiles that are 93% air bubbles.

5 Give two advantages of having lots of air bubbles in the tile material.

The picture shows a silica cube seconds after taking it out of a furnace at 1200 °C. The scientist can hold it at the corners because it conducts heat very poorly.

Tiles of this material lose 90% of their heat within moments. They are designed to absorb huge amounts of heat without increasing their temperature very much. They are used on areas of the space shuttle where the highest temperatures are generated during re-entry into the Earth's atmosphere.

Learn about

- The development of the space shuttle
- Problems with re-entry

▲ A shuttle launch.

▲ A shuttle landing.

How Scienceworks

A model of the space shuttle shows it glowing during re-entry. The glow is due to some of the tiles being heated until they are red- or white-hot.

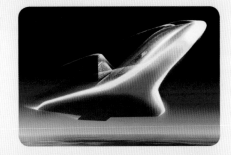

 6 Which part of the shuttle is hottest?

Flying!

Before a shuttle was launched into space it was tested by carrying it piggyback style on top of a Jumbo Jet. The friction with the air made the aluminium skin it was made from expand. This made 40% of its insulating tiles fall off!

 7 Why did the aluminium skin expand?

This gave scientists another problem to solve! The tiles covering the shuttle must be very close together.

 8 Why must the tiles be very close together?

The silica tiles are **brittle**; they cannot flex or bend without breaking. To let the structure flex, felt pads are sandwiched between the tiles and the structure. This lets the structure move without moving the tiles. A technician is shown mounting some of the 31–34 000 thermal protection tiles on a shuttle.

A sticky problem

The first shuttle to fly in space – *Columbia* – was launched from the Kennedy Space Centre in the United States on 12 April 1981. But when it made an aeroplane-style landing in California two days later, 16 of its heat-resistant tiles fell off and 148 were damaged!

The glue used to stick the tiles to the shuttle failed at the high temperatures of re-entry. Luckily the temperature inside the shuttle did not get high enough to harm the astronauts.

But it was back to the drawing board for the design team. They had to develop a new glue that would withstand the high temperature of re-entry. It took several attempts before they made a suitable one.

 9 What important property did the new glue need?

Get this

- Scientists and engineers had to develop new materials for the space shuttle.
- Very high temperatures are reached during re-entry. Astronauts inside the shuttle have to be protected.

10.1 What is light?

What is light?

Light is a way of transferring energy.

Light sources give out light. We say they are luminous. Here are two.

 1 Name two other sources of light.

Energy from light travels from a source through **waves**. These light waves do not need anything to travel through. This is why light can reach us from the Sun and other stars across the emptiness of space.

Infrared (heat) radiation is transferred through waves very similar to light.

 2 Why can we feel the Sun's heat even though there is no air between the Sun and Earth?

Light and shadows

Light waves travel in straight lines. Early morning light in a forest shows **rays** of light travelling in straight lines.

Shadows are formed because light travels in straight lines. Light cannot pass through the figures in the picture. The figures are **opaque**. Light is blocked by the figures casting shadows on the floor.

 3 Where is the light source that forms the shadows in the picture?

A small light source produces a sharp shadow called an **umbra**. A large light source produces an image with fuzzy edges. It has an umbra and a **penumbra**.

 4 How do you know that a small light source was used to produce the rabbit shadow?

5 Sketch the appearance of the rabbit shadow if a large light source was used.

Learn about
- What light is
- How light travels
- How we see light

How do we see things?

Non-luminous objects do not give out light. You only see them when light bounces off them into your eye. Most objects are non-luminous.

When you read a book under a lamp, light from the lamp hits the book. The light bounces off the page **(reflects)** and some of this reflected light enters your eye. Light also reaches the eye directly from the lamp.

Hitting objects with light

When light hits something it can:

- pass through – be **transmitted**
- bounce back – be **reflected**
- stay inside the object – be **absorbed**.

Light passes through **transparent** objects such as a clear glass window.

Frosted glass lets light through but breaks the light up so that you cannot see through it clearly. This type of glass is **translucent**.

 6   Suggest where you might use frosted glass.

An opaque object does not let light through it at all. When light hits an opaque object some light is reflected, which is how we see it. But most of the light energy is absorbed by the object. This makes the object heat up.

White and pale objects reflect most of the light shining on them. Black and dark objects absorb most of the light. Infrared (heat) radiation is reflected and absorbed in the same way as light.

 7   Which is the better absorber of infrared radiation, black or white?

8   Why do we tend to wear dark-coloured clothes in winter?

9   Why is it harder to see dark-coloured cars at night than light-coloured ones?

Summing up

10   Is the Moon a luminous or non-luminous object?

11   Draw a diagram to show how you can see the ball when playing football.

12   Sam wants to paint the outside of his house black to save energy. Do you think this is a good idea? Explain your answer.

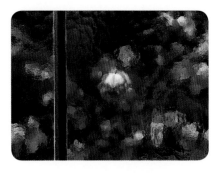

▲   A red flower behind frosted glass.

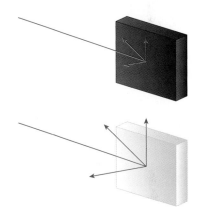

Get this

- Light is a wave, similar to infrared.
- Light travels in straight lines.
- When light hits an object it can be transmitted, reflected or absorbed.
- When an object absorbs light energy it heats up.

Learn about
- Reflection in a plane mirror
- Reflection from smooth and rough surfaces

Mirror, mirror on the wall

Beth is doing Amy's hair. Amy is looking at her **reflection** in a flat mirror, or **plane mirror**. Her reflection looks just like Amy. It is the right way up, the same size and the same colour.

When Amy moves her head closer to the mirror her **image** moves towards her.

 1 What happens when Amy moves her head away from the mirror?

Her image always appears to be the same distance behind the mirror as she is in front of it. But there is nothing behind the mirror; no light can get through it. It is an illusion. We say the image is **virtual** – a second Amy does not really exist behind the mirror.

Beth has her left hand on Amy's head.

 2 Which hand does Beth's reflection have on Amy's head?

If Beth's image was a real person standing opposite to her, they would have their right hand on Amy's head. The image in a mirror is **laterally inverted**; left becomes right and right becomes left.

 3 Car drivers keep an eye on the traffic behind them by looking at a mirror at the front to see out of the back window. Why is AMBULANCE written strangely in the photograph?

It's an illusion!

How do we see the image in a mirror? Light from the candle (the **object**) reflects off the mirror into your eye. Your brain knows that light travels in a straight line so it assumes the light has come from I. This is where you see the image.

 4 Is the image of the candle real or virtual? How do you know?

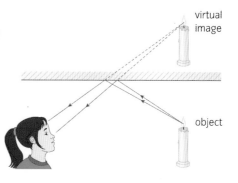

Two mirrors

The giraffe and the periscope both show two mirrors.

▲ These two mirrors are at right angles.

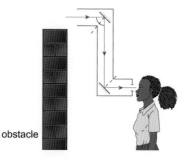

▲ These parallel mirrors are used to make a **periscope**.

5 How many images of the giraffe can you see?

6 Give one use of a periscope.

A question of angle

Light reflects off a shiny smooth surface such as a mirror in a regular way so you see a clear image of the object.

A ray of light hits a mirror at a particular angle. This is called the **angle of incidence (i)**. The angle is measured from an imaginary line drawn at right angles from the point where the ray hits. This line is called the **normal**. On a plane mirror the light ray then bounces off again at exactly the same angle, called the **angle of reflection (r)**.

Every light ray hitting the mirror does the same thing so that your eyes see a very accurate image of an object, but laterally inverted.

Light reflects off a rough surface in all directions so you don't see a clear image reflected in it.

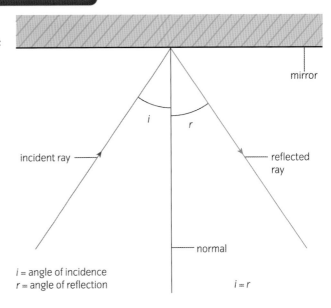

mirror

incident ray

reflected ray

normal

i = angle of incidence
r = angle of reflection

$i = r$

 7 Jo polishes her table. She can see her face reflected in it. What does the polish do?

a)

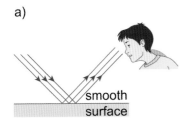

smooth surface

▲ Reflection from a smooth surface (**regular reflection**)

b)

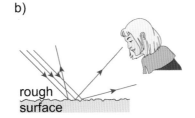

rough surface

▲ Reflection from a rough surface (**diffuse reflection**)

Summing up

8 Darren's nose is 30 cm in front of a plane mirror. How far is his nose from its image?

9 Ellie looks at her reflection in a plane mirror. Write down four facts about her image.

10 Draw a diagram to show how the images of the giraffe in question 5 are formed.

11 Look at the drawing of the periscope. What are the angles of incidence and reflection at each mirror?

Get this

- The image in a plane mirror is laterally inverted.
- The angle of incidence is equal to the angle of reflection.

Learn about
- Refraction of light
- Total internal reflection

Can light bend?

Is the straw in the glass of water really broken?

When light travelling through a transparent substance such as air meets a different one such as glass or water it changes direction. This 'bending' of light is called **refraction**.

The diagram shows why a swimming pool looks shallower than it really is. The light reflected off the rock at the bottom of the pool travels to the surface. When it moves into the air it changes direction.

When the light reaches your eye your brain assumes that it has travelled in a straight line from the rock. So you see it in a different place.

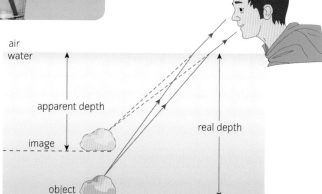

 1 Draw a diagram to show why your pencil looks bent when you dip it in water.

It's all about speed

In air, or in space, light travels at a speed of 300 million m/s. That's fast! No wonder we think we see things instantly. In glass it only travels at about 200 million m/s.

 2 How far does light travel through space in one hour?

When a ray of light goes into a denser substance like glass or water it slows down and changes direction. When it goes into a less dense one like air it speeds up.

"I didn't think my head would go under the water!"

How do we know... about refraction?

If you pass a narrow ray of light from a ray box through a glass block you can see that it changes direction.

When light enters the glass block its angle with the normal becomes smaller than its angle of incidence. This is its **angle of refraction**.

When the ray of light leaves the glass it speeds up and its angle with the normal changes again and becomes bigger.

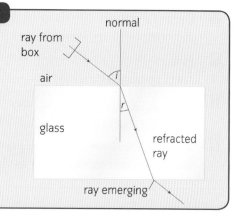

Total internal reflection

Sometimes light rays never leave the denser substance. They are reflected backwards and forwards inside it. This is called **total internal reflection**. Diamonds sparkle because the faces are cut so that light is totally internally reflected.

Optical fibres use total internal reflection. These are very thin flexible glass rods. Light reflects internally along their whole length. This means that any image at one end of the fibre can be communicated very clearly to the other end.

Optical fibres are used to see inside all sorts of places. Bundles of optical fibres, called an **endoscope**, are used to see inside the body.

How does total internal reflection happen?

When a light ray travels into a less dense substance its angle of refraction is always *greater than* the angle of incidence.

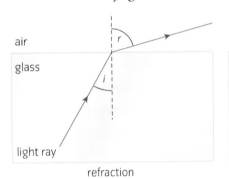

refraction

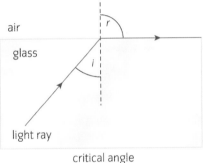

critical angle

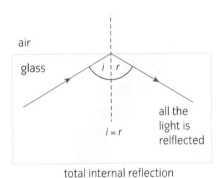

total internal reflection

- If the angle of incidence increases the angle of refraction increases too.
- If the angle of refraction reaches 90° the angle of incidence that has caused this is called the **critical angle**.
- If the angle of incidence is bigger than the critical angle **all** the light is reflected back into the glass. This is total internal reflection.

3 What can you say about the angle of incidence when a ray of light travels along an optical fibre?

Summing up

4 Does light travel faster or slower in water than in air?

5 What path does a ray of light follow if it enters a rectangular glass block at an angle of incidence of 0°?

6 A hunter is spear fishing. Why doesn't he aim his spear where the fish appears to be?

Get this

- Light changes direction when it passes into a substance with a different density.
- This is refraction.
- Total internal reflection can happen inside a dense substance like glass.

More light bending

Splitting light

When white light (ordinary sunlight) passes through a glass prism it changes direction but it also splits up, or **disperses**, into all the colours of the **spectrum**.

red **orange** yellow **green** **blue** **indigo** **violet**

Sir Isaac Newton did this experiment in about 1666. He named seven colours in the spectrum, though indigo is hard to spot between blue and violet. But Newton was interested in magic and seven was a mystical number.

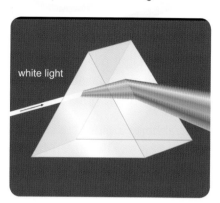

white light

Recombining colours

Some people suggested that the prism added the colours to the light. Newton proved them wrong. He showed that white light is made of the spectrum of colours by recombining these colours to make white light.

He used two triangular prisms, one to split white light and the other, placed upside down, to join the colours together again.

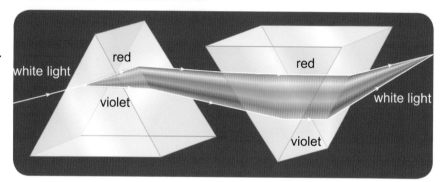

white light — red — violet — red — white light — violet

How do we think about... light?

What is light? Newton thought that light was a stream of particles. A Dutch scientist, Christian Huygens, who lived around the same time, was convinced that light is a wave.

- Newton's theory predicted that light would travel faster in water than in air.

- Huygens' theory predicted that light would travel slower in water than in air.

Their theories could be tested by measuring the speed of light in air and in water. But this was not possible at that time. Newton had a reputation as a scientific genius and so scientists adopted his theory. It was not until 1850 that a French scientist called Foucault showed that Newton was wrong!

1 As a result of Foucault's experiment did scientists decide that light is a particle or a wave?

2 Suggest why Newton's and Huygens' theories could not be tested in the seventeenth century.

▲ Newton.

▲ Huygens.

3 Why did passing the coloured light back through another prism show that it was not the prism colouring the light?

4 If this coloured disc is spun very quickly it looks white. Why?

5 Why is a triangular prism good for showing a spectrum?

Why does light split up?

The light slows down when it enters the glass prism. It disperses because all the colours that make up white light slow down by different amounts – red least and violet most.

This is because each colour has a different **wavelength** – the length of one wave. They are refracted by different amounts so they spread out.

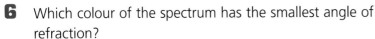

6 Which colour of the spectrum has the smallest angle of refraction?

▲ Red has longer wavelength than violet.

Rainbows

You see a **rainbow** when you are facing falling rain but with the Sun behind you. White light enters each raindrop and is split into its colours. The raindrops act a bit like the prism.

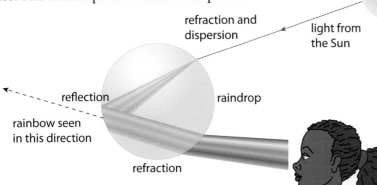

refraction and dispersion

light from the Sun

reflection

raindrop

rainbow seen in this direction

refraction

Summing up

7 Give two places, apart from a prism and a rainbow, where you might see a spectrum of colours.

8 Why was Newton's theory of light accepted for nearly 200 years instead of Huygens'?

9 What is the difference between refraction and dispersion?

10 How is the change in speed of the different colours that make up white light linked to the amount of refraction in a prism?

Get this

- White light can be split into a spectrum of seven different colours.
- This is dispersion.
- The colours of the spectrum can be combined to form white light again.

Learn about
- How we see colour
- Mixing coloured lights

How do we see?

When light from an object enters our **eye** it is refracted by the **cornea** and **lens**. It forms an image on the **retina**. This is like a screen at the back of the eye.

The eye lens can become fatter so that light from near objects is refracted to form a clear image on the retina. This image is upside down! The brain sorts this out so that we see things the right way up.

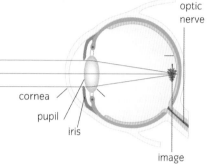

How do our eyes detect colour?

The retina has lots of light-sensitive cells called **rods** and **cones**. Rods are mainly around the edge of the retina and are sensitive to dim light. Cones are sensitive to bright light and colour, and are mainly in the centre. Rods and cones send messages to the brain along the **optic nerve**.

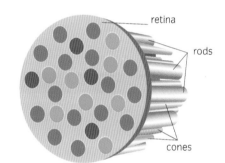

Some people's cones don't work properly and they don't see colours accurately. Very few people are totally **colour blind**. Imagine not seeing any colours at all! Much more common, especially among men, is a form of colour-blindness where greens and reds get mixed up.

 1 What problems might people have who are red/green colour blind?

This is a test for colour-blindness. If you have normal colour vision you will see a 7 and 4 in the dot pattern. If you have red/green colour-blindness then you will see a 2 and 1 revealed in the dots.

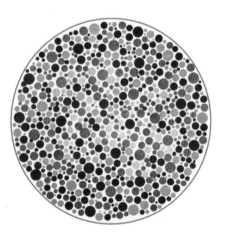

Coloured lights

Coloured filters are used to produce light of different colours.

A red filter only lets red light through. It absorbs light of all other wavelengths.

A green filter only lets green light through and absorbs the other parts of the spectrum.

Red, green and blue are called **primary colours**. All other colours can be made by combining these in various ways.

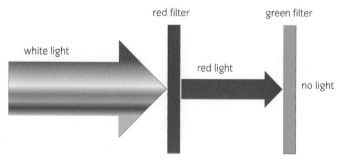

Magenta, cyan and yellow are **secondary colours**. They are made by combining two primary colours.

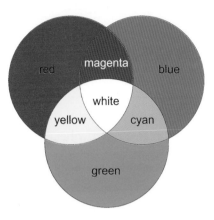

2 Explain why white light is produced if red, green and blue lights overlap.

3 Which primary colours overlap to produce yellow light?

Why does my apple look red?

The skin of a red apple contains a pigment that reflects red light but absorbs all other colours of the spectrum shining on it.

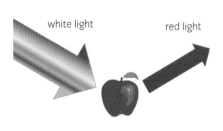

white light   red light

4 What colours in white light are absorbed by a green apple?

5 Why is Ed's T-shirt yellow?

Black objects absorb nearly all the light energy shining on them.

White objects reflect nearly all the light energy shining on them.

Things look different in different coloured light. If blue light is shone onto a red apple there is no red light to be reflected so the apple looks black.

6 What colour would the red apple look in green light?

7 What colour would Polly's and Ed's T-shirts appear in green light?

8 Tom is wearing blue-tinted sunglasses. What colour T-shirts does he think Polly and Ed are wearing?

Get this

- The retina of the eye has light–sensitive cells called rods and cones.
- Different coloured light has different wavelengths.
- Coloured objects reflect light of their own colour and absorb the rest.

Summing up

9 How does the eye lens change when we look at a distant object?

10 What would you see if you passed white light through blue and then red filters?

11 Why does grass look green?

12 What colour would the grass appear under orange street lights? Explain.

10.6 Using light

Learn about
- What is a laser?
- Using lasers

What is a laser?

One of the most useful ways of using light is a **laser**. This is a concentrated narrow beam of light of a single wavelength or colour.

A laser can concentrate a lot of light energy onto a very small area. This makes it a very powerful tool.

Never look into a laser beam!

 1 Why should you never look into a laser beam?

Using lasers

High-power lasers can cut out a shape or drill holes in metals.

Barcode scanners use low-power lasers.

 2 Lecturers often use laser pointers. How powerful do you think these lasers are?

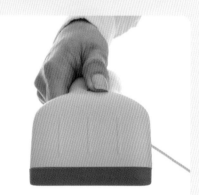

CDs and CD-ROMs

A **compact disc** (CD) stores data such as music. It has a series of tiny pits which is read by a low-power laser. To reflect the laser light, there is a fine film of metal coating the CD which follows the pits exactly. This metal layer is covered by another layer of transparent plastic which prevents dust and scratches spoiling the sound quality.

A CD-ROM works in the same way except the data is not music but instructions for a computer.

A more powerful laser is used to burn the pits into the CD or CD-ROM.

 3 Why can't the same laser be used to burn and read a CD?

Using lasers in medicine

Lasers are used to weld pieces of metal together. The laser melts the metal. The particles mix together and later solidify as one piece.

In a similar way doctors use lasers to 'weld' skin. The retina can sometimes be detached – it comes away from the back of the eye. A laser is used to 'weld' it back on.

4 How can a laser beam repair a detached retina?

In **keyhole surgery** surgeons can examine the inside of a patient's body and then treat the problem through a very small cut. They use a steel tube containing a bundle of optical fibres, a light and small surgical instruments, which can be moved by remote control. A powerful laser beam can be sent down one of the optical fibres to repair torn tissues or to remove a small growth.

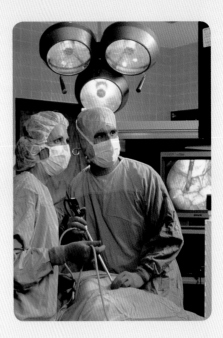

 5 How does light travel down an optical fibre?

6 What are the advantages of keyhole surgery compared with surgery where patients are cut open?

Dentists now use lasers to whiten teeth. They put a gel on the patient's teeth. The laser activates a bleach, hydrogen peroxide, in the gel.

A firefighter uses a laser to free a person trapped in a vehicle after a road traffic accident. The laser produces an intense beam of light that heats up the metal so that it can be cut away. A second firefighter holds the casualty still to prevent them making their injuries worse.

How do lasers work?

The first laser was made by Theodore Maiman in 1960. 'Laser' stands for **L**ight **A**mplification by **S**timulated **E**mission of **R**adiation.

Maiman made a helium–neon laser that gave out red light. Unlike the waves in ordinary light, the waves in a laser beam are all in step. This makes the laser beam very powerful. Laser light does not spread out.

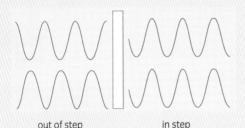

out of step   in step

Now lasers can produce many different colours, as well as infrared and ultraviolet radiation.

 7 What property of light does a laser show clearly?

8 Why can lasers be so powerful?

9 Suggest some advantages of using lasers instead of sharp cutting tools.

Brainache

Q A light bulb has a power of 60 W; a school laser has a power of only 1/1000 W. Why do we have to take care when using a laser?

A Its energy is concentrated on a very small area.

Get this

- A laser gives an intense beam of light.
- A laser can be powerful enough to cut metal.
- Lasers have many everyday uses.

Learn about
- How vibrations cause sound
- How we hear

In space no one can hear you scream!

It's not just in movies that there is no sound in space. In space there is no air to vibrate. Sound needs a material to travel through because sound is a **vibration**.

Sound travels better through solids and liquids than it does through air. That is why American Indians used to put their ears to the ground to listen for approaching horses.

 1 Dolphins can communicate with each other over much larger distances than humans can communicate. Explain why.

Astronauts have to use radio to communicate with each other when they are on the Moon or walking in space. It does not matter how loud they shout, they cannot be heard without radio.

 2 Why do astronauts have to use radio to communicate with each other on the Moon?

3 Two astronauts are on the Moon. They move close together so that their helmets touch. They can now hear one another without radio. Suggest why.

Earthquakes make a lot of noise. The sound travels through the Earth and is detected by sensitive microphones buried in the ground. These inform scientists about earthquakes.

Good vibrations

All sounds are caused by vibrations. In a loudspeaker, a paper cone vibrates.

It is difficult to see the cone vibrate, but you can sometimes feel it. Small polystyrene beads will bounce around and show the vibration of the cone.

The prongs of a tuning fork vibrate. If the ends of the prongs are dipped into water, you can see the effect of the vibration. The vibrations transfer energy.

The sound from a tuning fork is very quiet when you strike it. Place the stem of the fork on a table and the sound is much louder. This is because the whole table top is now vibrating. It does not move much, but it makes a much larger amount of air vibrate.

Energy transfer

Sound transfers energy as a wave. Imagine sound travelling from a loudspeaker to an ear.

As the loudspeaker vibrates, the layer of air next to it vibrates as well. This causes the next layer to vibrate, and so on. All of the layers of air between the loudspeaker and the ear vibrate backwards and forwards. This is a wave.

4   Use a particle model to explain why sound travels faster through solids than it does through gases. (*Hint:* think about how close the particles are in solids and gases.)

How do we show... sound waves?

We cannot see a sound wave, but a slinky spring shows how a wave works.

compression   rarefaction

Move one end of the spring backwards and forwards in the direction of the arrow. The coils move closer together then further apart again as the wave transfers energy. Where the coils of the spring are closer together it is called a **compression**. Where the coils are further apart is a **rarefaction**.

I can hear you

When the sound vibrations reach you, they move through your ear to your **eardrum**. The vibrating air makes the eardrum vibrate in exactly the same way as the air and the loudspeaker vibrate.

The vibrating eardrum makes other structures deep inside your ear vibrate. One of these structures changes the vibration into electrical signals that the brain recognises as sound.

Summing up

5   What happens to air in a compression of a wave?

6   A loudspeaker plays a musical note by vibrating 256 times each second. How many times does the eardrum of a boy, listening to the note, vibrate each second?

Get this

- Sound is caused by objects vibrating.
- Vibrations transfer energy as a wave through solids, liquids and gases.
- Sound cannot travel through a vacuum.
- The ear changes vibrations into electrical signals that the brain recognises as sound.

Learn about
- Loudness of sound
- How to reduce sound levels

Sound levels

It is almost impossible to go anywhere without being surrounded by **noise**. Scientists define noise as 'unwanted sound'.

We measure sound in a special unit called the **decibel (dB)**. A sound level of more than 140 dB can permanently damage your hearing.

Sound level in dB	Example of sound	Effect
0	threshold of hearing	cannot be heard
10	soft whisper	can just be heard
20	bedroom	very quiet
30	library leaves rustling	
40	talking quietly village street	quiet
50	office noise	disturbs conversation
60	normal speech telephone ringing	intrusive
70	restaurant background music	difficult to use telephone
80	home stereo traffic at junction	annoying
90	lawnmower lorry	can damage hearing after 8 hours per day
100	jet taking off 500 m away	can damage hearing after 2 hours per day
110	electric drill thunder	can damage hearing after 15 minutes per day
120	rock concert	
130	pneumatic drill air raid siren	painful
140	gun shot jet engine 30 m away	loudest recommended level with ear protection
150	trumpet 15 cm away	possible permanent ear damage

1 How loud would you expect the noise to be in your school library?

2 Why can it be harmful to live under the flight path of aircraft as they take off from an airport?

On the decibel scale, an increase of 10 dB means that the sound is twice as loud. This means that a lawnmower is twice as loud as a home stereo. If your ear is 15 cm away from a trumpet, then that is four times louder than a pneumatic drill.

 3 How many times louder is an air raid siren than a lorry?

Harmful to health

More people than ever are complaining about noise. As well as lorries, cars, planes and trains, it could be noisy neighbours, noisy people going home from the pub, church bells or a cockerel crowing in the morning.

Recent studies by the World Health Organization suggest that the stress caused by noise may cause as many as 3300 deaths a year in England from heart disease.

Noise levels may also cause poor performance at school. Primary schools with too much noise outside have failed to meet government targets for Maths and Literacy.

Keep the noise down

Houses near to airport runways often have double glazing fitted and paid for by the airport. Double glazing cuts down the noise getting into the house. Trees are planted alongside main roads that are built near to houses.

 4 Why are houses near to airport runways fitted with double glazing?

People who work in noisy environments must wear **ear defenders**.

 5 Suggest three jobs where people should wear ear defenders. Use the table showing sound levels to help you.

There are even jobs around the home that can damage your hearing if you do not wear ear defenders.

Summing up

6 Suggest one reason, other than tiredness, why lorry drivers are not allowed to drive more than an average of 48 hours per week.

7 Many of the early disc jockeys suffered from poor hearing later in their lives. Suggest why.

8 Suggest why children at a primary school near to a busy airport may not do as well in their Key Stage 2 tests as children at a primary school in the middle of a country village.

9 Suggest why trees are planted next to a motorway that runs close to a housing estate.

Express & Echo

CHURCH'S CHIMING CLOCK IS TIRESOME INTRUSION

A woman has called for the chiming clock of a town church to be silenced overnight so she and her husband can get some sleep. The clock at the parish church chimes on the hour and every 15 minutes and has done so for over 150 years. Now the woman wants it silenced between 7pm and 9am.

Get this

- Sound levels are measured in decibels.
- Loud sounds can be damaging to hearing and to general health.
- Sound levels can be reduced by double glazing or wearing ear defenders.

Learn about
- Frequency and pitch
- Audible range

Frequency and pitch

The number of times a guitar string or loudspeaker vibrates every second is the **frequency** of the vibration.

Frequency is measured in **hertz (Hz)**. Middle C has a frequency of 256 Hz, and top C has a frequency of 512 Hz.

Musicians often refer to the **pitch** of a note. A high-pitched note has a high frequency. A low-pitched note has a low frequency.

 1 Sharon plays middle C on her guitar. How many times does the string vibrate each second?

Audible range

Young people can usually hear sounds between 20 Hz and 22 000 Hz. This is known as the **audible range**.

As people get older, their audible range changes and they can not hear the higher frequencies. By the time you reach 30, you may only be able to hear up to 16 000 Hz.

Imagine, being able to hear things your parents and teachers cannot hear!

Some shopping centres use sounds that only young people can hear to prevent antisocial behaviour.

They have a device called the mosquito that makes sound with a frequency of between 17 500 Hz and 18 500 Hz. The sound level is 85 dB at a distance of 1 m. It can be heard from 15 to 20 m away.

When the security officer thinks there might be trouble from young people gathered nearby, the device is switched on. It automatically switches off after 20 minutes.

It's OK. The ringtone was too high for the teacher to hear.

 2 Look back at the effect of different noise levels on page 128. What effect does the mosquito's noise have on young people?

3 Some people say that using the mosquito is wrong. What are the advantages and disadvantages of using the mosquito?

Other animals

Not all animals can hear the same range of frequencies as humans. Some can hear lower frequencies, some can hear higher. Some have a narrow range, some a wide range.

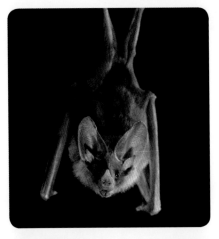

Species	Audible range in Hz
bat	2000–110 000
canary	250–8000
cat	45–64 000
chicken	125–2000
cow	23–35 000
dog	67–45 000
dolphin	1000–100 000
elephant	16–12 000
ferret	16–44 000
goldfish	20–3000
guinea pig	54–50 000
hedgehog	250–45 000
horse	55–33 500
mouse	1000–91 000
owl	200–12 000
rabbit	360–42 000
rat	200–76 000
sheep	100–30 000
whale	1000–123 000

4 What is the lowest frequency a goldfish can hear?

5 What is the highest frequency a dolphin can hear?

6 Which animal has the largest audible range?

7 Which animal has the smallest audible range?

Summing up

8 Dog whistles make a tone with a frequency of 30 000 Hz. What is the advantage of this?

9 Three people and two animals share a house.

The highest frequency Annie can hear is 15 000 Hz.

The highest frequency Bertie can hear is 45 000 Hz.

The highest frequency Charlie can hear is 20 000 Hz.

The highest frequency Danni can hear is 18 000 Hz.

The lowest frequency Eddie can hear is 16 Hz.

Identify the child, the parent, the grandparent, the dog and the ferret.

Get this

- The pitch of a note depends on the frequency of the sound wave.
- The audible range is the frequencies of sound an animal can hear.
- Animals have different audible ranges.
- The audible range gets smaller with age.

131

Echo

Sound is a wave. All waves can be reflected when they hit surfaces.

Reflected sound is called an **echo**. You hear an echo if you stand in front of a tall cliff or building and make a loud noise.

How long it takes to hear the echo depends on how far away you are.

Stopping echoes

In a large room or theatre, sound reflects off the walls, floor and ceiling. Sometimes the echo will last for several seconds as the sound bounces around the room. This is called **reverberation**.

If you are at a concert, you don't want to keep hearing the echoes. Theatres are designed to absorb as much unwanted sound as possible. Soft materials such as curtains and carpet absorb sound. Hard materials such as wood and concrete reflect sound and cause echoes. Some venues have absorbent structures attached to the roof.

 1 Why do cinemas and theatres have curtains hanging along the walls?

How's baby doing?

Pregnant women can see pictures of their baby before the birth. About the 12th week of pregnancy, the woman has an **ultrasound** scan of her womb to check the development of the fetus.

Ultrasound is sound with a very high frequency, above the audible range of humans.

X-rays are not used because they could harm both the fetus and the mother. They also only reflect from hard surfaces such as bone.

The frequency of the ultrasound can be as high as 10 000 000 Hz (10 megahertz or 10 MHz).

Learn about
- Echoes
- Ultrasonic scanning
- Uses of ultrasound

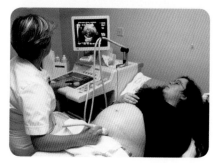

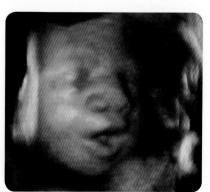

Ultrasound reflects from the boundaries between soft tissues as well as from hard surfaces so it can show a detailed picture of the fetus.

Some ultrasound scanners are able to produce a three-dimensional picture of the fetus.

2 What are the advantages of taking a picture of a fetus in the womb using ultrasound instead of X-rays?

Using the speed of sound

$$\text{speed} = \frac{\text{distance}}{\text{time}}$$

Sound travels at about 300 m/s in air. If you are 150 m away from a cliff when you shout, the sound takes 0.5 s to reach the cliff and another 0.5 s to get back to you. You hear the echo 1 s after you shout.

 3 Ben is using a starting pistol at the school sports day. He fires the pistol and hears an echo off the school building 1.5 s later. How far away from the building is he?

Ships use ultrasound to detect submarines, or shoals of fish, or to map the sea bed. They use a device called **sonar**.

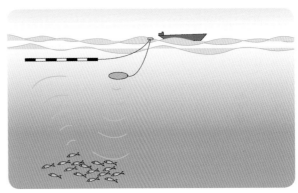

The ship trails a sound generator and some sensitive microphones. The sound generator produces a pulse of sound which travels through the sea and reflects off anything it meets. The microphones detect the reflected pulse. The time it takes for the reflected pulse to come back is used to calculate the depth of the object.

 4 The speed of sound in water is 1500 m/s. The microphones trailing behind a boat detect a reflected pulse from the sea bed 4 s after it was transmitted. How deep is the sea bed?

Estate agents and surveyors use an ultrasound distance meter to measure the size of rooms and other on-site distances.

The meter sends out a pulse of ultrasound which is reflected from the opposite wall.

Summing up

5 What is an echo?

6 There is less reverberation in the school hall when it is full of students than when it is empty. Explain why.

7 Why can't we hear ultrasound?

8 Describe how a ship might try to find a sunken wreck.

Get this

- Echoes are reflected sound.
- The time taken to detect an echo allows distances to be measured.
- Ultrasound is high-frequency sound above human hearing.
- Ultrasound has many medical and industrial uses.

Learn about
- How sound is produced by musical instruments
- Musical notes

String along

To play a stringed instrument such as the guitar you pluck or strum the strings. The frequency of the note depends on:

- the length of the string – a long string makes a lower note than a short one
- the thickness of the string – a thick string makes a lower note than a thin one
- the tension in the string – a loose string makes a lower note than a tight one.

 1 How does a guitarist change the length of a string as he plays the guitar?

2 How does a guitarist change the tension in the string of a guitar?

To play the violin you use a bow or pluck the strings. The bowing of the strings makes them vibrate along their length, as well as up and down. This is why the violin has a different sound from a guitar.

▲ Playing the guitar.

▲ Playing the violin.

Blow me!

When you blow across the top of a bottle, the air in the bottle vibrates and makes a sound. If you add water to the bottle and blow again, the pitch of the note becomes higher.

The pitch of the note depends on the length of the air column in the bottle. The shorter the air column, the higher the pitch.

Wind instruments have a vibrating reed, or the person playing the instrument vibrates their tongue. The length of the vibrating air column is controlled by opening valves or by changing the length of the instrument.

 3 How does a trombone player produce different notes from her trombone?

4 Why does a fife produce a very high-pitched note?

▲ Playing the trombone.

Beat that!

The science of percussion instruments such as drums is not as simple as you may think. The note produced depends, among other things, on:

- the diameter of the drum
- the depth of the drum
- whether the drum has a skin both top and bottom or just on the top
- what type of drumstick you hit the drum with.

▲ Playing the fife.

In general, the larger the diameter or deeper the drum, the lower the pitch of the note.

Timbre

Each instrument makes a different sound even if they are playing the same note. Why?

The answer is that every note from an instrument has more than one frequency. The main frequency is called the **fundamental**.
But other frequencies are also produced which may be twice, three times, four times or even more times the fundamental frequency. These are called **harmonics**.

So although you hear the fundamental frequency as the note, you are also hearing other frequencies as well without realising it.
These different harmonics make the distinctive sound of that instrument which is called its **timbre**.

How do we know... that notes have harmonics?

You can look at musical notes if you connect a microphone to an **oscilloscope**. The display shows the timbre of a note.

5 The note produced by the clarinet is 256 Hz. What is the fundamental frequency of the notes produced by the saxophone and violin?

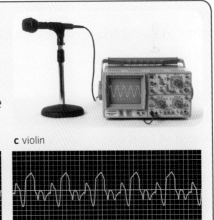

a clarinet

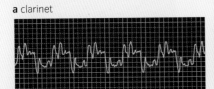

b saxophone

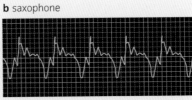

c violin

The first musical instrument

The first musical instrument we use is our own voice.

We produce sound, and just like any other instrument, it is the timbre that makes us unique. When we speak to a friend on the phone, we recognise their voice. Imagine having to ask each time who you were speaking to?

Summing up

6 The vibrating string on a violin is very quiet. What other part of a violin vibrates?

7 A drummer can change how tight the skin is on his drum. What happens to the pitch of the note if he tightens the skin?

Get this

● Musical instruments produce sound in a number of ways.
● Different instruments make different sounds even when playing the same note.

How fast?

Light travels at a speed of 300 000 km/s (300 000 000 m/s).

Sound travels much slower, about 300 m/s in air. It travels faster through liquids and solids.

? 1 How many times faster is the speed of light compared with the speed of sound?

Unless we look at very distant objects, the time light takes to reach our eyes is negligible. Light from the Moon only takes just over 1 s to reach us.

But when we listen to sounds that are only 100 m away, there is a noticeable delay.

If you watch someone hammering in fence posts across the other side of a field, you hear the sound of the hammer hitting the post after you see it happen. The hammer might seem to make a noise on its up swing!

Using the speed of sound

Knowing about the difference between the speed of sound and the speed of light is very important. Timekeepers at sports events start their stopwatches when they see the smoke from the starting pistol, not when they hear the bang.

? 2 Linford and Kelly are timing the 100 m sprint at the school sports day. They are standing 100 m away from the starter. Linford starts his stopwatch when he sees the smoke from the starting pistol. Kelly starts her stopwatch when she hears the bang. The two runners they are timing finish the race together.
(a) Whose stopwatch records the *correct* time?
(b) What is the difference between the times on the two stopwatches?

How do you know how close a thunderstorm is? You always see lightning before you hear the thunder. Count the seconds between the lightning and the thunder. For every 3 s, the storm is 1 km away.

? 3 Maria counts 12 s between seeing the lightning and hearing the thunder. How far away is the storm?

4 What will Maria notice when the storm is directly overhead?

Learn about
- The speed of sound and the speed of light
- Travelling faster than the speed of sound

How Science Works

Supersonic

When you travel faster than the speed of sound, you are travelling at **supersonic** speed. It's often called 'breaking the sound barrier'.

 5 Which *two* of these speeds are supersonic?

    200 m/s   300 km/h   400 m/s   1500 km/h

Scientists say that something travelling at the speed of sound is travelling at **Mach** 1. A plane travelling at Mach 2 has a speed of 600 m/s.

 6 How fast is a plane travelling if it is at Mach 2.5?

Try to imagine travelling faster than the speed of sound. You are 600 m away from your friend and shout to them that you won't be much longer. The sound takes 2 s to reach them.

But if you are travelling at twice the speed of sound, you will get to them in only 1 s. Will you both hear your shout after you have arrived?

The first attempt to set a land speed record in a car was in December 1898 when a top speed of 17.6 m/s (39.25 miles per hour) was recorded.

Nearly 100 years later, in October 1997, the *Thrust* SSC set a new record of 341 m/s (763 miles per hour). It was the first car to travel faster than the speed of sound.

Some military aircraft break the sound barrier. Only two passenger aircraft have broken the sound barrier. The Anglo-French plane Concorde was the most famous one. It cut the record journey time from New York to London to just under 3 hours.

In July 2000, 113 people died when a Concorde crashed in Paris. Then there were other safety problems and the number of people travelling across the Atlantic fell. Some flights were less than half full.

British Airways and Air France had to stop flying the plane because it no longer made a profit.

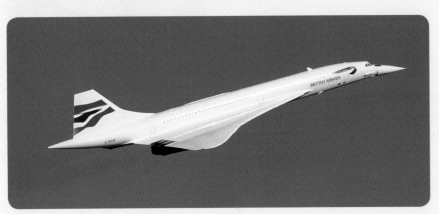

Get this

- Sound travels much more slowly than light.
- Supersonic vehicles travel faster than the speed of sound.

Learn about
- Turning forces
- Using levers as machines

A turning question

A see-saw is one example of a **lever**. The see-saw works best if both children weigh about the same.

 1 Weight is a force. What unit is used to measure weight?

Sarah's weight causes the lever to go down on the right. Joe's weight causes it to go down on the left. The see-saw turns around the **pivot** in the middle.

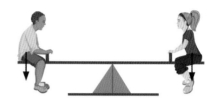

We talk about it turning **clockwise** or **anticlockwise**. The force from Sarah moves it clockwise and the force from Joe moves it anticlockwise.

If both children weigh about the same, the **turning effect** at each end is similar and the see-saw works well. But what happens when Joe's dad sits on one end?

Joe's dad can balance the see-saw, but he has to move towards the pivot. This is because the turning effect is affected by how close he is to the pivot as well as his weight.

 2 Look at the diagram. What happens to Joe's dad's turning effect as he moves closer to the pivot?

The rule is that the further you are from the pivot, the more turning effect you have. Because of this, we can use levers to lift or move weights much greater than our own weight. We call these levers **force multipliers**.

The ancient Greek philosopher Archimedes knew about levers and how they worked. He said:

'Give me a lever long enough, and a place to stand, and I will move the entire Earth.'

 3 Why is it not really possible to move the Earth with a lever, no matter how long it is, or how strong the force is on the other end?

Using levers

Levers in see-saws are for fun but most levers mean business! We use them as force multipliers to shift things we couldn't move otherwise. The thing we are moving is called the **load**, and the force we provide is called the **effort**.

Levers do not always look like see-saws, and they are not always straight bars.

Often the pivot is between the load and effort, as in a see-saw. If the pivot is nearer to the load, we need less effort to move the load. A claw hammer is an example of this type of lever.

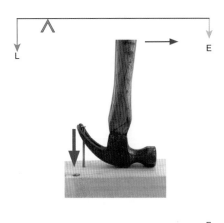

4 Which colour arrow represents the load and which colour arrow represents the effort?

5 The distance from the pivot to the hand is larger than the distance from the pivot to the nail. Which force is larger – the load or the effort?

Sometimes the load is between the pivot and the effort.

The distance from the pivot to the effort is always bigger than the distance from the pivot to the load.

This means that we use less effort than if we tried to move the load without the help of a lever.

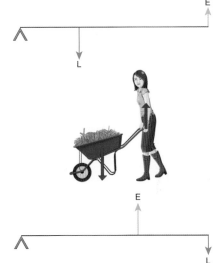

Sometimes the effort is between the pivot and the load. This means that the effort is always bigger than the load.

Using tongs to turn the meat on the barbecue uses more effort than if you don't use tongs.

6 Why use tongs?

Calculating moments

The turning effect of a lever is called the **moment**. The moment depends on both the force (or weight) and the distance to the pivot:

moment = force × distance between force and pivot

Here is an example. Sunita weighs 350 N and sits 1.6 m from the pivot of a see-saw. This means her moment is:

350 × 1.6 = 560 Nm

Sunita's mum weighs 700 N and sits 0.8 m from the pivot of the see-saw. This means her moment is:

700 × 0.8 = 560 Nm

So the see-saw is balanced.

Summing up

7 Sketch a diagram to show how you can use a screwdriver to lever the lid off a paint tin. Label the load, effort and pivot.

8 Why is it easier to lever a paint tin lid off with a screwdriver than it is with a coin?

9 David weighs 250 N and Jane weighs 300 N. They sit 2 m from the pivot of a see-saw. How far away does their mother have to sit if she weighs 500 N?

Get this

Levers:
- have a pivot, load and effort
- can help move large loads with small efforts
- can make a force act at a greater distance.

Learn about
- Time periods
- Using pendulums

Backwards and forwards

A swing at the playground and the pirate ship at a theme park both behave in the same way. They are both **pendulums**.

The time it takes to swing backwards and forwards is called the **period**. A pendulum is stationary at each end of its swing and is travelling fastest at the lowest point of its swing. We normally time the period of a pendulum as it passes through its lowest point. This is because we don't know when it has reached the end of its swing until it has stopped and started to come back the other way.

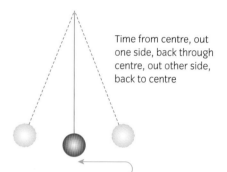

Time from centre, out one side, back through centre, out other side, back to centre

How long does it take?

Ian times his friends on the swing in the park. He thinks that a heavier person will swing faster. The swing's period will be shorter. He also thinks that pushing the swing harder will mean a shorter period.

He times each of his friends as they swing 10 times. Here are his results.

Name	Weight in N	Time for 10 swings in s	
		Gentle push	Hard push
Abbie	380	27.8	28.9
Brenda	433	28.0	27.4
Colin	439	27.7	27.3
Danni	496	28.6	28.4
Erika	496	28.0	27.9
Frank	508	29.0	27.5
Gary	522	27.1	28.6
Harry	532	28.2	28.0

1 Look at Ian's results. Do they agree with his predictions? Explain why.

2 What has Ian found out from his results?

Back in the school laboratory, Ian makes a pendulum. He ties a small weight (bob) onto a length of cotton.

The length of a pendulum is measured to the **centre of gravity** of the bob.

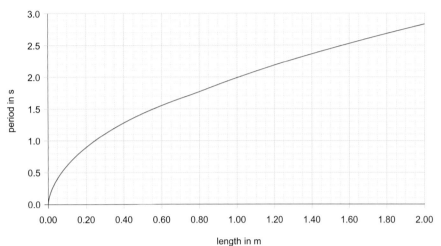

He measures the period of the pendulum as he changes the length. He plots a graph of period against pendulum length.

 3 What is the period of a pendulum when it is exactly 1 m long?

4 Ian wants a pendulum to swing backwards and forwards once every second. How long should he make it?

Keeping time

The period of a pendulum increases as the length increases. Some clocks rely on pendulums to keep accurate time. But there is a problem. Clock pendulums are usually made from metal.

 5 What happens to metals when they are heated?

6 What happens to the length of a pendulum in summer?

7 What happens to the period of a clock pendulum in summer?

8 Does a clock gain or lose in summer?

The clock at the Houses of Parliament in London has to keep very accurate time. The chimes of Big Ben are broadcast throughout the world.

The length of the pendulum is nearly 4 m.

Pennies are placed on top of the pendulum bob to make sure the clock keeps accurate time. Adding a penny shortens the length of pendulum and makes the clock run faster by 0.8 s per day.

Summing up

9 What is the period of a pendulum?

10 How is the period of a pendulum related to how hard the pendulum is pushed?

11 What happens to the clock at the Houses of Parliament if a penny is removed from the pendulum bob?

Get this

Pendulums:
- have a time period that does not depend on mass but does depend on length
- can be used for very accurate timing.

Round and round

Forces can change the shape, speed or direction of an object.

An object either stays still, or moves in a straight line at a constant speed, unless a force acts on it.

 1 What happens to the speed of a car when there is a greater thrust from the engine?

2 Max is pushing a box along the floor. What happens to the direction the box is moving if Milly starts to pull?
Draw a diagram to show how the box moves.

Imagine a skater on an ice rink. There is almost no friction to slow her down. If she is pushed, she will keep moving for a long time.

Now imagine she is holding onto a very slippery pole. There is almost no friction between her and the pole. Now when she is pushed, she will go round and round the pole in a circle.

There is a force changing her direction the whole time.

 3 In what direction is the force acting?

4 If she lets go of the pole, in which direction will she move?
Choose A, B or C.
A towards the pole   **B** in the same circle   **C** in a straight line

Centripetal force

Imagine taking pictures from above the skater as she moves in a circle.

When the first picture is taken, she is moving in the direction **X**.

When the second picture is taken, she is moving in the direction **Y**.

The skater has changed direction. As she moves in a circle, there is a force acting the whole time. This force is the **tension** in her arm holding the pole. It acts towards the centre of the circle and is called the **centripetal force**.

Believe it or not, you probably learned a lot about circular motion when you were very young. The roundabout in the playground is probably one of your earliest memories of circular motion.

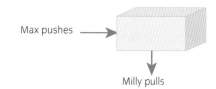

Max pushes

Milly pulls

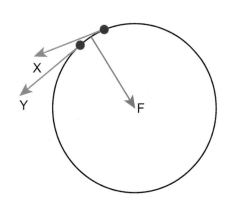

X

Y

F

And you were probably swung round in a circle like this.
What happens as the child is swung round in a circle?

 5 In which direction does the force act on the child?

6 What if the adult lets go of the child? In which direction does the child now move?

The adult does not usually let go of the child. But the hammer thrower does let go of the hammer.

She spins the hammer round her head then spins herself before letting go. This is to make the hammer travel as fast, and therefore as far, as possible.

 7 In which direction does the hammer go when it is thrown? Choose **P**, **Q** or **R**.

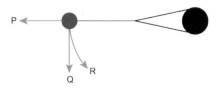

Space circles

The International Space Station is one of many satellites in orbit above Earth.

Planets orbit the Sun.

Everything needs a centripetal force to keep it in orbit.

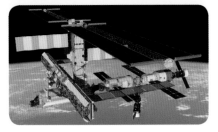

8 What is the source of the centripetal force that keeps the International Space Station in orbit around Earth?

Summing up

9 What is the source of the centripetal force that keeps Earth in orbit around the Sun?

10 James is on a roundabout in the playground. It is turning around. He jumps off from point **X** towards **B**. Where will he land? Choose **A**, **B**, **C** or **D**.

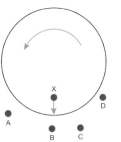

Get this

To keep things moving in a circle:

● the direction changes. This is caused by a force.

● there is a force towards the centre of the circle. This is called the centripetal force.

Drop it

If you drop a hammer and a feather at exactly the same time, which lands first?

In July 1971, the *Apollo 15* commander, David Scott, tried this on the Moon. When he dropped a hammer and a feather together, they hit the Moon's surface at the same time. Why?

On Earth, the feather has more **air resistance**. Air resistance is a **frictional force** between the feather and the air. This slows it down, a bit like a parachute. The Moon has no air. Without air resistance everything falls at the same rate.

 1 What force pulls things to the ground?

Drop slide

Not many people choose to fall to Earth without a parachute. The nearest we come to this is a drop slide. This Demon Dropslide at Flambards in Cornwall looks like a vertical drop but is really a cleverly constructed curve. You are always in contact with the slide. There is friction between you and the slide. Friction is a force acting against gravity.

 2 In which direction is the frictional force acting?

The frictional force increases as the slide becomes less steep, and you slow down safely.

Measuring falls

 3 What happens to the frictional force and your speed if you slide down a water-coated drop slide?

The water slide in the picture is 37 m high. The boy will reach a top speed of 25 metres per second (m/s) as he falls. But he doesn't go this fast at the start – he goes faster and faster as he falls.

 4 At his top speed, how many metres would the boy travel in one second?

This happens to any falling object. When you drop a tennis ball, it falls to the ground. At the moment you drop the ball, its speed is zero. As it falls, it speeds up. It is **accelerating**. Its speed increases by 10 m/s every second. This acceleration is caused by gravity.

5 Lizzie drops a cricket ball from a hot air balloon into the sea.
- **a** What is its speed 4 s after she drops it?
- **b** What is its speed 2.5 s after she drops it?

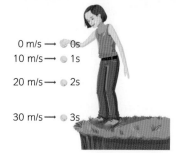

0 m/s — 0s
10 m/s — 1s
20 m/s — 2s
30 m/s — 3s

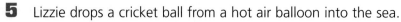

As its speed increases, the distance the ball falls every second also increases. This is shown in the graph.

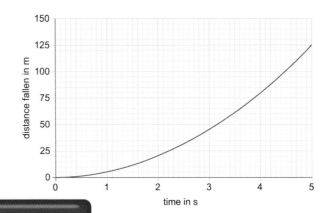

 6 How far does the ball fall during the first 3 s?

7 How long does it take for the ball to fall 100 m?

8 What is the ball's *average* speed over 5 s?

Skydiving

The Red Devils are a parachute display team. They jump from an aeroplane about 3 km above the Earth.

As they fall to Earth they accelerate, but air resistance acts against them as they fall.

- Air resistance increases as you get faster.
- The bigger the area moving through the air, the larger the air resistance.

Eventually the force of gravity is **balanced** by the force of air resistance and the skydivers stop accelerating. They fall at a constant speed called **terminal velocity**. This is nearly 200 km/h (50 m/s).

They are still falling very fast. To land safely they need to slow down. They open their parachutes. This increases their air resistance and slows (**decelerates**) them to under 10 m/s.

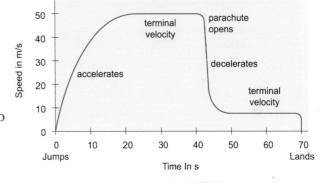

 9 At what speed would the skydivers hit the ground if they did not open their parachutes?

Get this

Falling bodies:
- all accelerate at the same rate provided we ignore air resistance
- are slowed down by friction
- reach terminal velocity.

Summing up

10 Explain why you come down a dry slide faster if you sit up than if you lie down flat.

11 The first display team skydiver out of the aeroplane falls out flat. The last skydiver comes out head first. Suggest why.

Under pressure

Which would hurt most if it stepped on you – a 3 tonne elephant or the stiletto heel worn by a 50 kg woman?

Answer: the stiletto heel.

The whole of the woman's weight is concentrated onto one very small area. The elephant's weight is much greater, but its foot has a much larger area. The weight is more spread out.

The pressing down from the foot or heel is called **pressure**. Pressure depends on two factors:

- force
- area of contact.

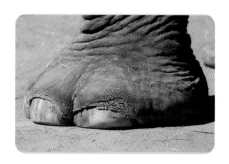

You are always exerting pressure on surfaces around you, whatever you are doing.

 1 Wooden dance floors can be damaged by dancers wearing stiletto heels. Why?

2 Explain why drawing pins do not need much force to push them into a notice board.

Low pressure

People who trek across snow wear snowshoes.

 3 How does the pressure exerted by the snowshoes compare with the pressure exerted by normal shoes?

4 What would happen if someone set off in deep snow without wearing snowshoes?

Skiers and snowboarders also need to have large surface areas. Water skiers need the large surface area of their skis to stay on top of the water.

 5 Look at the pictures of the feet of a camel and a wading bird. Why are their feet shaped the way they are?

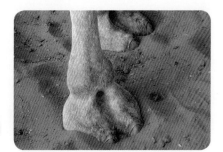

How do we show... the effect of pressure?

Freeze a block of ice in an ice cube tray.

Rest the ice on a strip of wood across the bath.

Make a weight by filling a milk container with water and hang it over the block of ice with a loop of very thin wire.

The wire passes through the ice, but the ice block remains intact.

The pressure of the wire melts the ice. This allows the wire to pass through the water. The water refreezes as it comes into contact with the remaining ice.

6 Why does the thin wire exert so much pressure on the ice?

High pressure

Ice skaters do not skate on ice!

Ice is dry, and its surface is quite rough. The blades on the skates are very thin. This means there is a small area in contact with the ice.

7 How does the pressure exerted by the skate blades compare with the pressure exerted by normal shoes?

8 What happens to the ice as a skater moves? (*Hint*: think about the experiment above.)

9 Why does this allow skaters to move smoothly across the ice?

Measuring pressure

We can calculate pressure like this: **pressure = force/area**

The unit of force is the newton (N). Area is measured in metre squared (m^2) so pressure is measured in newton per metre squared (N/m^2). Another name for the newton per metre squared is the **pascal** (Pa).

10 What happens to the pressure if the force increases?

11 What happens to the pressure if the area increases?

Summing up

12 John uses two different pieces of wire to cut through identically sized blocks of ice. He hangs the same weight on each wire. One wire is much thicker than the other. Which wire passes through the ice first? Explain why.

13 Amy does the same experiment but with two identical pieces of wire. She hangs a much heavier weight on one of the pieces of wire. Which wire passes through the ice first? Explain why.

14 Lindsey's back garden has an area of 50 m^2. The weight of air in the atmosphere above her garden is 5 000 000 N. Calculate the pressure of the air on each square metre.

Get this

Pressure depends on:
● force
● area of contact—
A large force causes a larger pressure than a small force.
A large area causes a smaller pressure than a small area.

Weight changes

On many thrill rides you feel a force similar to those felt by astronauts as they blast off, or by fighter pilots as they pull out of a steep dive. This is because of the sudden changes in speed and direction during the ride.

The average adult can go from feeling lighter than a model to heavier than a sumo wrestler in a matter of seconds.

Think about what happens to you when you take a ride in a lift.

You get into the lift on the ground floor and press the button to go up.

Your body has **inertia**. This is the reluctance of something stationary to start moving, and its reluctance to stop once it is moving.

1 The force on the lift causes it to accelerate upwards. Your body is reluctant to start moving. As a result, you push down more on the floor of the lift as it rises beneath you. You feel heavier.

   A 500 N girl will appear to weigh 550 N when the lift accelerates upwards.

2 When the lift is moving at a steady speed, the forces on it are balanced.

   Your weight returns to normal.

   You feel the same as you do when the lift is stationary.

   The 500 N girl appears to weigh 500 N.

3 At the top, there is a force on the lift causing it to slow down.

   Inertia means that you are reluctant to slow down.

   As a result you feel lighter.

   The 500 N girl appears to weigh 450 N.

On the way down, the reverse is true.

When the lift accelerates downwards, you feel lighter and as it slows down at the bottom, you feel heavier.

In some very fast lifts, you may find your legs buckle as the lift starts moving up and when it slows on the way down.

It is not just you who feels heavier. Anything you carry will also feel heavier. Imagine carrying a heavy pile of books!

 1 How much will the 500 N girl appear to weigh in the lift as it accelerates downwards from the top floor?

2 How much will the 500 N girl appear to weigh in the lift as it slows down when it reaches the ground floor?

If the lift cable snapped, the lift and the girl in it would fall freely.

The girl would not exert any force on the floor of the lift; she would appear to be weightless.

3 How much will a 500 N girl appear to weigh in a lift if it is falling freely?

Pulling G

Scientists talk about **pulling G**. This is how much heavier than your normal body weight you appear to be. If you appear to be twice your normal body weight, then you are pulling 2G.

The Knightmare Roller Coaster at Camelot Theme Park has the highest value of any roller coaster in the UK. At one point on the ride you pull 5G.

 4 Jamie weighs 450 N. What will his maximum weight appear to be on the Knightmare Roller Coaster?

I want to be an astronaut

Astronauts train in a specially adapted aircraft. During a series of dives the trainee astronauts feel weightless for up to 30 s. A typical flight lasts 2 hours. By the end of the flight, they will have spent 20 minutes feeling weightless.

The rapid acceleration when rockets launch means that astronauts feel up to 7 times heavier. Thrill rides are not too far short of this, so get training!

 5 Visit the websites of some theme parks. Work out which rides will make you feel the heaviest or lightest.
(*Hint*: look for the highest and the fastest.)

Get this

Rapid changes in speed can result in you feeling heavier or lighter.

Glossary

A

absorbed to take in a liquid, gas or other substance from the surface or space around

absorbs the conversion of energy of electromagnetic radiation, sound, etc. into other forms of energy on passing through a medium

accelerating the rate of change of increasing speed

acid chemical compounds which produce hydrated hydrogen ions h+(aq) when in aqueous solution

adapted has, over many generations, developed physical features or behaviours which suit its environment

addictive something containing a chemical that changes your brain in a way that makes it difficult for you to stop taking it

AIDS (acquired immune deficiency syndrome) caused by the HIV virus, which is transmitted through the exchange of body fluids

air resistance a force which pushes against things that are moving

alkali metals elements in the first group in the periodic table

allergic a condition in which the body produces an abnormal immune response to certain allergens, including dust, pollen, certain foods, drugs and fur

alloy a mixture of two or more elements (usually metals except for carbon in steel)

alveoli tiny thin–walled air sacs in your lungs where oxygen diffuses in and carbon dioxide diffuses out

angle of incidence the angle between the incident ray and the normal line

angle of reflection the angle between the reflected ray and the normal line

angle of refraction the angle between the refracted ray and the normal line

antibiotic a substance that destroys bacteria

antibodies substances produced by white blood cells which help your immune system to recognise and destroy microbes

anticlockwise the opposite direction to the movement of the hands of a clock

antiseptics chemicals used to destroy microbes on your skin or in cuts

artery a thick-walled blood vessel that carries blood away from the heart under high pressure

audible range the range of frequencies that the human ear can hear

B

bacteria single-celled microbes with a cell wall but no nucleus

bioaccumulation an increase in the concentration of chemicals, such as pesticides, moving along the food chain from producer to carnivore

biodegradable describes any substance which can be broken down by natural processes of decay

biodiesel fuel produced from renewable resources

biofuels plant materials or animal waste which can be used as fuel resources

biological weathering the disintegration of rock and mineral due to the chemical and/or physical agents of an organism

bleach a chemical used to destroy microbes on surfaces

brittle hard but easily broken

C

cancer a disease caused by cells dividing in an uncontrolled way

cannabis a type of hallucinogenic drug

capillary the narrowest type of blood vessel

cementation the gluing together of particles of sediment

centripetal force the force directed towards the centre that causes a body to move in a uniform circular path

cervix the neck of the uterus at the inner end of the vagina

chemical weathering the dissolving and breakdown of rock by chemical reactions

chlamydia a sexually transmitted infection (STI) which can stop a woman having babies later

cilia a minute hair like structure on the surface of some cells used to sweep materials along tubes

claystone a fine-grained sedimentary deposit which has silicate chains interspersed with aluminium ions (aluminosilicate)

clockwise moving around in the same direction as the hands of a clock

clot a collection of fibres and red blood cells that seals a cut in a blood vessel

colour blind a genetic disease affecting colour vision and results from a malfunction of certain cone cells in the retina of the eye

compact disc a metal disc on which high-quality digital recordings can be made

compounds the substance formed by the chemical combination of elements in fixed proportions, as represented by the compound's chemical formula

compression the squashing together of particles

conduction the way in which heat energy is transferred through solids (and to a much lesser extent in liquids and gases)

constipated unable to push waste material out of the gut

consumer an organism that does not make its own food

convection the way in which heat energy is transferred through liquids and gases by movement of the particles in the liquid or gas

convection current the way in which heat energy is transferred through liquids and gases by movement of the particles in the liquid or gas

cornea the transparent layer at the front of the eye

critical angle the smallest angle of incidence at which total internal reflection occurs

crystals pure solids with a regular lattice structure giving a regular polyhedral shape

cytoplasm the part of a cell between the membrane and the nucleus where chemical reactions take place

D

decelerates the rate of change of decreasing speed

decibel (dB) a commonly used unit of sound intensity or loudness)

degrees Celsius (°C) a temperature scale based on the lower fixed point of ice at 0°C and the upper point of steam at 100°C

depressant a drug that slows your reactions

desert an area where very little rain falls

diarrhoea an illness which makes your faeces more watery than normal

diffuse what the particles in gases and liquids do when they move from where there are a lot of the particles to where there are fewer

diffusion is the way particles in liquids and gases mix or spread out by themselves

digestive system the collection of organs that digest food

disinfectants chemicals used to kill microbes on surfaces

disperses the splitting up of a ray of light of mixed wavelengths by refraction into its components

donor a person who donates blood, other tissues or organs

E

ear defenders used to protect the ears from noise

eardrum a membrane which transmits sound vibrations from the outer ear to the middle ear

echo a reflection of sound wave by an object so that a weaker version is detected after the original

effort physical exertion to create force

element substance consisting of atoms of only one type

embryonic stem cells embryos developed from eggs that have been fertilised by IVF

emits send out (heat, light, vapour etc.)

endangered species a plant or animal species in immediate danger of extinction

energy needed to make things happen

enzyme a substance used to break down large insoluble food molecules

erosion the removal of the weathered parts of rock

ethical an action that is morally right

exchanges see gas exchange

expands increases in size

eye the organ of sight, which focuses and detects

F

faeces a solid composed of undigested food and bacteria that is eliminated through the anus

fats food molecules that are high in energy

fertiliser any substance that adds minerals to soil

fitness the ability of your heart, lungs and blood vessels to deliver extra oxygen to your cellsflu an infection cause by a virus

force multiplier a lever which can lift or move weights much greater than own weight

formula a way of showing elements using symbols

freeze-thaw weathering form of physical weathering common in mountains and glacial environments

frequency the number of complete waves produced in one second(measured in hertz)

frictional force a force that resists movement

fundamental the lowest note of a chord in its original form

fungus a type of microbe that can cause infections

G

gas exchange when your blood swaps carbon dioxide for oxygen in your lungs

genes you inherit these from your parents and they influence the way your body develops

genetic engineering a technique used to add extra genes to an organism

genetically modified (GM) a living thing that has had extra genes added to it from another organism

glucose a simple sugar used for respiration - formed when carbohydrates are broken down in your digestive system

gonorrhoea a sexually transmitted infection (STI)

grains seeds eaten as cereals or used to make bread

group elements in the periodic table

gullet the section of your gut that connects your mouth and stomach

H

habitat a place where a plant or animal lives

hallucinogen a drug which distorts your senses so that you see things which aren't real

halogens elements of the periodic table

harmonics frequencies of a wave which are multiples of the fundamental frequency

heart attack when your heart stops beating because the blood supply to some of its muscle cells has been cut off by a blockage in an artery

heat the sum of the total energies of all the particles

herbicide a chemical compound used to kill unwanted plants or weeds

herbivore animals like cattle, deer, rabbits and sheep which feed on plants

hertz (Hz) the SI unit of frequency

HIV (abbreviation for human immunodeficiency virus) is the virus which causes AIDS

HPV a virus transmitted through sexual contact

I

igneous rock formed when magma from the inside of the earth's crust crystallises

image the point from which rays of light entering the eye appear to have originated

immune able to resist infection

immune system a system within an organism that protects against disease

immunised given a vaccine to increase your immunity to a specific disease

inertia the tendency of an object to resist a change in speed caused by a force

infrared radiation the way that heat energy is transferred from a hotter to a colder place

insect an invertebrate with three pairs of legs and two pairs of wings like a beetle

insecticide a chemical compound used to used to kill insects

insulin a hormone used to control blood glucose levels

J

joules (J) the unit of energy

K

keyhole surgery a surgical technique using small incisions

L

large intestine the part of the gut between the small intestine and rectum that houses beneficial bacteria and removes water from undigested food to make solid faeces

larvae the juvenile stage in the life cycle of many invertebrates e.g. caterpillars, grubs or maggots

laser a device that produces an intense beam of light that does not spread out

laterally inverted the type of reversal that occurs with an image formed by a plane mirror

lava hot liquid rock that comes out of a volcano

lens device made of shaped glass which focus light rays from objects to form an image

lever a simple machine consisting of a rigid bar supported at a point along its length

light a form of energy emitted by luminous objects like the sun

light sources (luminous objects) are objects which emit visible light

limestones a form of sedimentary rock

load an external force which acts over a region of length, surface, or area

M

Mach the ratio of the relative speed to the speed of sound

magma hot molten rock that originates from the Earth's mantel

melting point the temperature at which a solid changes into a liquid

meningitis a disease in which tissues enclosing the brain and spinal cord become infected and swollen, causing severe headache, fever and sometimes death

metals one of a group of elements having certain similar properties

metamorphic rock rock formed by the action of intense heat on sedimentary or igneous rock

microbes organisms which are too small to be seen without the aid of a microscope

minerals natural inorganic substances which are needed for building certain body tissues

minerals naturally occurring inorganic substances

molecule the smallest part of a substance that can

take part in a chemical reaction

moment a measure of the ability of a force to rotate an object about a pivot

MRSA a health care-acquired infection that can be found in hospitals

mucus a thick liquid that is produced in parts of the body, such as the nose

mudstone a type of sedimentary rock

N

National Health Service (NHS) the organisation that provides health care throughout the UK

natural polymer a polymer produced by a living organism

nicotine an addictive stimulant found in cigarettes

noble gas noble gases occupy around 1% of the atmosphere

noise any undesired sound

non-luminous objects which produce no light

non-metals elements that are not metals

non-porous not able to let through air or water

normal an imaginary line at right angles to a surface where a light ray strikes it

nucleus the cell's control centre that contains genes

nutrients are substances from food which are essential for healthy growth

O

obese having a higher than average body mass – usually as a result of eating too much sugar and fat

object something that can be seen or touched

opaque objects which absorb, scatter or reflect light and do not allow any light to pass through

optic nerve a paired sensory nerve that runs from each eye to the brain

optical fibres uses total internal reflection to transmit light along very fine tubes of plastic or glass

P

paramedic a person who helps the sick or injured but who is not a doctor or a nurse

peer pressure pressure exerted by a group of people in encouraging a person to change their attitude, behaviour and/or morals

peers people of the same age, status, interests, etc.

pendulum any rigid body that swings about a fixed point

penumbra the area of blurred or fuzzy shadow around the edges of the umbra

period the time taken to complete one cycle of motion

periodic table an arrangement of elements in order of increasing number of protons (atomic number)

pitch a property of sound determined by its frequency

pivot short shaft, or pin, on which something turns or oscillates

plane mirror a mirror with a reflective surface

plankton minute organisms that drift or float in water

plaque a sticky film of food debris which forms on teeth after meals

polymer a substance having large molecules

polythene an addition polymer formed by up to 50 000 ethene molecules

predator an animal that hunts, kills, and eats other animals

pressure a continuous force applied by an object or fluid against a surface

primary colours with respect to light are any of red, blue and green

probiotic dietary supplements containing potentially beneficial bacteria or yeasts

producer an organism that can make its own food

proteins large molecules found in food which are essential for growth and repair

pulling G how much heavier than your normal body weight you appear to be

R

rainbow an optical phenomenon that appears as the colours of the spectrum when falling water droplets are illuminated by sunlight

rainforest where trees can grow fast, tall and very close together because the climate is hot and wet

rarefaction the spreading apart of particles

reactive to show a chemical change when mixed with another substance

reactivity series a list of metals placed in order of their reactivity

rectum the last section of the gut where your faeces are stored until you go to the toilet

red blood cells have no nucleus - used to carry oxygen from your lungs to your body cells

re-entry the return of a spacecraft into Earth's atmospehere

reflected to throw back light etc. from a surface

reflection the change in direction of a light ray after it hits a surface and bounces off

reflects the return of all, or part of, a beam of particles or waves

refraction the change in direction of a light ray as a result of its change in velocity

resistant to withstand the effect or action of a force

respiration a chemical reaction that releases energy in living things by converting glucose and oxygen into carbon dioxide plus water

retina the layer of light-sensitive cells at the back of the eye

reverberation the persistence of a sound for a longer period than normal

rock cycle shows how igneous rock forms sedimentary rock or metamorphic rock

S

saliva a liquid produced by your salivary glands which lubricates food as you chew it

salmonella a bacterium that causes food poisoning

sandstone a type of sedimentary rock

Sankey diagram a scale diagram that shows all the energy transfers taking place in a process

scavenger an animal that feeds on dead plants or animals

secondary colours with respect to light are colours that can be obtained by mixing two primary colours

sedimentary rocks formed by the deposition of particles

sedimentation the settling of solid particles through a liquid

sediments matter which has settled to the bottom of a liquid

selective breeding producing offspring with desirable features by controlling which animals breed over many generations

semiconductor a conductor whose electrical resistance decreases as the temperature rises

semi-metal a class of elements intermediate in properties between metals and non-metals

sewage is waste water from homes and factories which contain faeces, urine, used washing water and rainwater

sexually transmitted infections (STIs) diseases that are passed from one individual to another during sexual intercourse

shadows an area of darkness on a surface

silicones polymers containing chains of silicon atoms alternating with oxygen atoms

small intestine the part of your gut between the stomach and large intestine where most digestion takes place and nutrients pass into your blood

social animals a group of animals that interact with each other

sonar a system which uses ultrasound to detect underwater objects or to determine the depth of the water

space shuttle a reusable spacecraft for carrying people and cargo into earth orbit and then returning

species a group of organisms that can produce fertile offspring

spectrum a band of colours produced by separation of the colours in white light

starch a large carbohydrate molecule

stem cells cells found in most, if not all, multi-cellular organisms and are characterised by the ability to renew themselves through cell division

sterilised to make free of living organisms

stimulant a drug which speeds up your reactions and makes you more alert

stomach where food is stored and mixed with acid and enzymes before it enters your small intestine

strata the layers formed in the arrangement of the components of sedimentary rocks and soils

subconsciously the part of the mind that is not fully conscious but influences actions, etc.

sustainable development energy use that can be supported by renewable resources

symbol a sign which represents something

synthetic polymer a substance such as plastic, or a man-made fibre such as nylon and terylene

T

TB (tuberculosis) an infectious disease of the lungs

temperature the degree of hotness or coldness of something

tension the strained condition resulting from forces acting in the opposite direction

terminal velocity the velocity reached by an object when its gravitational force is equal to the frictional forces acting on it

thermal imaging camera a device that forms an image using infrared radiation so that different temperatures appear as different colours

thermal insulators something that prevents heat from moving from one place to another

thermals a rising current of heated air

thermogram a record of the image made by a thermal imaging camera

thermometer an instrument which is used to measure temperature

timbre the quality or 'timbre' of a sound is a result of the harmonics which are present

tissue matched cells from different people that are very similar

total internal reflection the complete reflection of light at a boundary between two media

transition metals the block of metallic elements in the middle of the periodic table

translucent objects that transmit light but diffuse (scatter) the light as it passes through

transmitted when light or other radiation passes

through an object

transplant transfer of living tissue, or an organ, and implant in another part of the body or another body

turning effect when a force causes an object to turn

U

ultrasound a sound above the human hearing range

umbra the area of total shadow behind an opaque object where no light has reached

unreactive not reacting chemically

uplift when huge forces from inside the Earth push rocks upwards to make mountains

V

vaccines part of a microbe used to make you produce antibodies so that you will be immune to that microbe in future

vacuum a space in which there is no matter

variation differences between living things

vertebrate animals with backbones

vibrate to move continuously and rapidly to and fro

vibration motion to and fro of the parts of a liquid or solid

villi finger-like projections which line the wall of the small intestine

virtual an image which cannot be focused onto a screen because rays of light do not actually pass through the image

viruses microbes which have genes but no cells – they can only reproduce inside living cells

vitamins compounds found in foods which are needed in small amounts to maintain health

vomiting eject matter from the stomach through the mouth

vulcanologist someone who studies volcanoes

W

wasted energy where energy is transferred to non-useful forms, often heat, which transfers to the air

water treatment works the process of removing contaminants from water

wave a variation of radiation through a medium or vacuum

wavelength the distance between two identical points on the wave, e.g. two adjacent peaks or two adjacent troughs

weathering is the wearing down of rocks by the environment

white blood cells used to detect or destroy microbes in your blood and tissues